THE DAWN OF MAN

D1314768

When the French amateur archaeologist Boucher de Perthes found some ancient flint tools at Abbeville in 1846, he declared: "These rude stones prove the existence of man as surely as a whole Louvre would have done." Only in recent times have archaeologists begun to piece together the story of man in a scientific way. Apart from De Perthes, the pioneers included men like John Frere, Georges Cuvier, and Charles Lyell in the eighteenth and nineteenth centuries.

In this addition to the PUTNAM PICTORIAL SOURCES SERIES, the authors show how, despite the Piltdown and other forgeries, modern archaeologists have followed in the footsteps of the early pioneers and achieved a much clearer view of man's origins and development. They present a wide range of graphic material upon which recent findings have been based. They outline the nature and extent of fossil evidence, vividly interpreted in the reconstructions of Maurice Wilson and others reproduced in these pages, and trace how the first toolmakers and hunting communities evolved in America, Africa, Europe, and elsewhere, showing what archaeological sites have revealed of ancient burials, primitive art and technology, and assess the links between primitive art and religion. The later sections of the book describe the slow evolution of the first agricultural communities out of which man's early civilizations were born.

Archaeologists today draw upon the services of many experts—geologists, petrologists, pedologists, geochemists, and others—in the search to perfect dating methods and other operations. The authors explain how their combined expertise has helped us study man's early history and identify the various stages of evolution reached by primitive groups in the modern world.

An engraving of a face made by Australian Aborigines
thousands of years ago in the Cleland Hills of Central
Australia (page 94)

A PUTNAM PICTORIAL SOURCES BOOK

THE DAWN OF MAN

VINCENT MEGAW AND RHYS JONES

G. P. PUTNAM'S SONS   NEW YORK

The Putnam Pictorial Sources Series

Copyright © 1972 by Wayland (Publishers) Ltd
This edition first published in 1972 by G. P. Putnam's Sons,
200 Madison Avenue, New York, N.Y. 10016
All rights reserved. This book, or parts thereof, must not be
reproduced in any form without permission
Published simultaneously in the Dominion of Canada by
Longmans Canada Limited, Toronto
Library of Congress Catalog Card Number: 76—185489
Filmset in England by Keyspools Ltd, Golborne, Lancs.
Printed in England by C. Tinling & Co. Ltd, London and Prescot

CONTENTS

INTRODUCTION

MOST BOOKS have a beginning, a middle and an end; here we are only concerned with the beginning—the dawn of man and the society and material culture he developed in the first stages of his still continuing evolution. In the following pages very little mention will be made of the great civilizations of the past; the artistic glory that was Greece has been discarded so that we may examine, however briefly, the very beginnings of art itself. The architecture of Rome has also been ignored so that we can illustrate the first simple huts of Stone Age hunters.

This book is not about the thin veneer of our civilization, but about the previous two million years of savagery. We live today in the Age of Technocracy, the age of the computer and nuclear fission; yet we are as much the cultural heirs of the first farming communities of some nine thousand years ago as we are of the priest kings of Egypt and Mesopotamia, the skilled Chinese town-dwellers of the second millennium B.C., and the pre-Hispanic nobles of the Andes who built their huge citadels without the aid of the wheel or any metal implements. The development of man as a social animal cannot be divorced from his biological development. Both must be related to the changing natural world around him—a world in which with the aid of his developing technology, man gradually ceases to be a slave to his environment, although he is still not completely its master.

Our survey ends at the point which many people still mistakenly consider the beginning of man's cultural history: the growth of an urban and frequently literate civilization and the parallel development of political systems and the city-state, well-known to all students of ancient history. It is the change from food gathering to food production, from man the hunter to man the farmer, which marks a decisive point in man's cultural development (see Table II, page 123).

The substance of our survey is "prehistory", the reconstruction of man's past by mainly other than documentary evidence. The techniques for a study of prehistory are the techniques of that magpie of scientific and humane studies, the archaeologist, who is not only concerned with "the study and practice of writing the history of man from material sources" but whose ultimate goal is to explain human behaviour in terms of the cultural systems of the past. We must remember that the techniques of the modern archaeologist apply just as much to a study of our most recent past as they do when considering the first tool-makers of Africa. The archaeological record starts the moment you throw an empty tobacco tin into the wastepaper basket. Thus the historian of colonial Virginia, no less than of ancient China or industrial England, turns more and more to the techniques of the archaeologist to fill in the holes in the patchwork quilt of his incompletely surviving written sources.

Man's view of his own past has matured together with other aspects of his expanding universe. Unfortunately, however, it is still true that to most people the history, let alone the prehistory of Man, means the history of Western man. It may not be a disadvantage that the two authors of this survey, though brought up and educated in the Old World, now live and work in the last area of the southern hemisphere to be touched by Old World culture, an area where one can still observe groups of food-gatherers in a vital period of transition. In the United States, prehistory has always been regarded as a simple extension of anthropology, that proper study of mankind. It was the confrontation in the sixteenth century A.D. of the Old World with the primitive societies of the New World which largely contributed to the gradual acceptance of the idea of the existence of similar primitive groups in the distant past. Three centuries after the establishment of European colonies in the Americas, the first anthropological studies of Australian Aborigines, and in particular their art, strongly influenced the final acceptance of the humanity of Cave Man.

More refined methods of analysis, including the use of powerful modern computers, may seem at first glance to have led to a "de-humanising" of the study of ancient man. However, these more sophisticated techniques of modern archaeology give us a more complete picture of the past than was possible just by using the individual theories and value-judgments of the pioneering art-historians and archaeologists of the last 150 years.

Finally, it may reasonably be asked: "Why should we bother to concern ourselves with the primitive and far-distant past?" For some, it is probably enough to say, like the proverbial mountaineer, that we tackle the problem "because it is there". Even more honest perhaps was the reaction of one Adult Education student, a bank manager, who studied archaeology "to get away from it all"! Beyond the search for knowledge for its own sake, there is something to be gained from studying man's past. Without knowledge of the dawn of man, we can never hope to understand those cultural processes which, in different parts of the world at different times, have evolved into that unique way of life which we now call "civilization".

CHAPTER ONE

ANGELS, APES AND MAN

MAN HAS LONG BEEN A HISTORICAL ANIMAL —he has also long been a snapper up of unconsidered trifles. Pieces of coal have been found, not as fuel but as play-things, in an Upper Palaeolithic mammoth hunter's camp site in Central Czechoslovakia; ancient potsherds were collected by Pueblo Indian villagers. Among the great literate urban civilizations, both the ancient Chinese and the Greeks were concerned with the reconstruction of their own past, albeit reconstructions peopled with mythical beings as well as simple men and women. However, even such an inveterate traveller and story-monger as Herodotus, "father of history", has a fair claim to having established the ethnographic approach to the past. The idea that anything old is necessarily better than anything new is not something for which we can just blame parents and school teachers. The poet Hesiod, writing in the Homeric era of the eighth century B.C., formed a view of the past consisting of the successively degenerating ages of gold silver, bronze and iron. In this, he foreshadowed the first nineteenth century experiments in classifying prehistoric artefacts. In the Middle Ages the Bible became the touchstone against which all scholastic thought was compared. As early as the twelfth century A.D., a Sephardic Jew from Tudela in Spain identified ruins in the neighbourhood of Mosul as the site of ancient Nineveh.

The European Renaissance from the fourteenth century onward revived interest in the classical foundations of Western civilization, and in the physical remains of the ancient world. In this respect, sixteenth century Italy has a fair claim to having been the nursery of the new study of archaeology. Yet the Bible still limited belief in a far distant past. For what was there before Julius Caesar, before the Druids built Stonehenge— which in fact they didn't? Who lived in Britain before Brutus, the grandson of Aeneas, had settled there—as Geoffrey of Monmouth suggested in the twelfth century and Nennius three centuries before him? The Lost Tribes of Israel and the Phoenicians, without the benefit of archaeological evidence, were both found a place in the crowded Northern Isles, while the origins of the Welsh were firmly associated with the building of the Tower of Babel. But even with the expanding frontiers of geography and reason in the eighteenth century, the past was seen very much in terms of the present. The first seeds were sown for a hardy perennial of archaeological thought, the idea that all cultures sprang from a single source. In the New World, while the Lost Tribes of Israel were invoked yet again to explain man in the Americas before Columbus, the "lost cities" of Central America were seen as vestiges of long vanished civilizations divorced from the contemporary Indian population.

It was science—or more precisely the

growth of geology, botany, and biology —which finally broke through the barrier of chronological disbelief. In 1797, John Frere, a Norfolk antiquary and Fellow of the Royal Society of London, told how he found objects of a time "beyond that of the present world". These we now know were Lower Palaeolithic hand-axes made certainly, as Frere said, "by a people who had not the use of metals". A century before, a similar claim by a London apothecary had been dismissed out of hand. In the mid-nineteenth century, investigators of the Somerset caves of southwestern England included a schoolmaster William Pengelly. Pengelly's geological knowledge enabled him to understand his discoveries at Brixham, where flints worked by human agency were found together with the bones of the extinct hyena, mammoth, and rhino. William "Strata" Smith's book, *Strata Indentified By Organized Fossils* (1816), laid the foundations for stratigraphic geology; and Charles Lyell, author of the great *Principles of Geology* (1830–33), did much to discredit the old "catastrophic" beliefs which referred back to the Biblical Flood. The climate was almost ripe for belief in "antidiluvial" man. Father McEnery, who had also excavated in the Devon caves in the 1820s, had been discouraged in his claim that tools found near Torquay were as old as the bones of extinct animals. Then, in 1836–37, a French customs official, Boucher de Perthes, investigating the gravel terraces of the River Somme, started outlining evidence for the undoubted association of flint implements of "diluvial" or "prehistoric" date. It was twenty years, though, before such men as the English geologist John Prestwich and archaeologist John Evans had vindicated the claims of Boucher de Perthes. By 1859, the year Prestwich addressed the Royal Society on the subject of the Somme gravels, antidiluvial man was legitimized —at least in the minds of most scientists. 1859 was also the momentous year of the publication of Charles Darwin's *Origin of Species*. Three years earlier, with the discovery of some human long bones and a skull cap fragment at Neanderthal near Dusseldorf, the world had been introduced to antidiluvial man himself.

It must be remembered that Darwin's ideas, which reached their climax in his *Descent of Man* (1871), were not the only ones concerned with an evolutionary sequence. The systemization of prehistoric artefacts had long antedated the storm which blew up over Darwin's apparent usurping of the functions of the Almighty by the process of natural selection. In 1816 the Dane Christian Thomsen, worked out a tripartite system of classification equivalent to three successive major periods or "ages"—the ages of stone, bronze, and iron. With the new evolution of a chronological view of ancient man and his artefacts, archaeology had truly come of age.

9

THE MEDIEVAL VIEW OF THE WORLD. Man's view of his past has always been coloured by what he knows of the present. The Flemish painter Hieronymous Bosch (*c.* 1450–1516) symbolizes the haunting fear of hellfire and witchcraft which was so much a part of his times; whatever Freudian imagery may be detected in such pictures as his *Earthly Paradise* (page 41), the art historian can also see elements of contemporary popular and religious imagery. Likewise, in the Middle Ages the great figures of ancient times are always shown wearing contemporary regional dress. A Persian miniature of *c.* 1425 depicting Alexander the Great arriving at the World's End (1) is as clearly a thing of its age as the illustration of the building of the Tower of Babel from a French book of hours made for John of Lancaster, Duke of Bedford (page 42). It tells us more about medieval building tech-

1

2

3

niques than about the historical truth of the Old Testament story. After the Renaissance, despite the growing awareness of the past, Christian beliefs still largely controlled this awareness. Using calculations by Martin Luther and the astronomer Johann Kepler, Bishop James Ussher (2) in his *Annals of the Old and New Testament* (1650) (3) maintained that the creation of the earth took place in 4004 B.C. Into such a framework had to be fitted all the relics of long lost cultures, such as the Bronze Age temple of Stonehenge (4). This most famous of all European prehistoric monuments was explained in its first known published illustration—in a fourteenth century history of England—as the work of the magician Merlin who is said to have transported the stones from Ireland in A.D. 483 (5).

4

5

THE GROWTH OF GEOLOGY. In the sixteenth and seventeenth centuries, scholars began to study the structure of rocks and the fossils contained in them. It was slowly realized that fossils were not thunderbolts or "sports of nature", but that they were the petrified remnants of once living plants and animals. Early examples of recognized fossils were these shark's teeth and corals (6), and ferns in coal measures (7) in Colonna's *Glossopetrae* (1616).

The major problem was how to explain the presence of plant and animal remains within the rocks. It was once suggested that they had been placed there by the Devil to try and tempt enquiring man away from the path of true faith! A major theory proposed by the French palaeontologist, Baron Georges Cuvier (1769–1832) (8), involved a series of great catastrophies, the last of which was the Flood of Genesis; this was supposed to have cast up

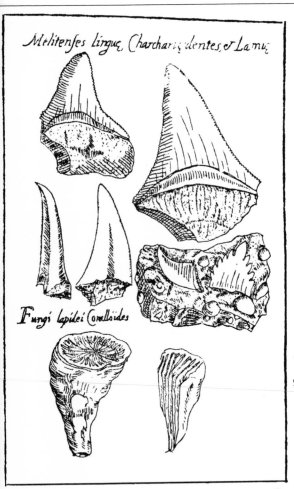

Melitenses lingue, Charcharis dentes, et Lamie

Fungi lapilei Coralloides

6

8

9

7

shells and fishes, together with the mud of the ocean floor, to form high mountains. A different approach was followed by the English engineer William Smith (9) who, while building canals near Bristol, noticed that the rocks were laid down in regular strata. He mapped the outcrops of these strata (10), and laid the foundations of modern sedimentary geology. British geologists proposed the "Principle of Uniformity", which stated that rocks had been laid down, lifted to mountains, and eroded down again, by exactly the same physical processes as can be observed today. This meant that the geological time scale had to be enlarged enormously to be measured in terms of tens or even hundreds of millions of years. This work was systematized by the Scot, Charles Lyell (11) in his masterpiece the *Principles of Geology* (1880–83).

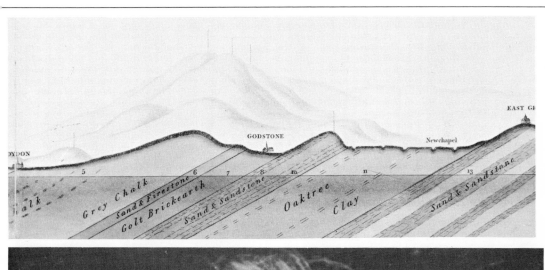

THE NOBLE SAVAGE. The conquest of South America by a handful of Spaniards destroyed ancient cultures as soon as they were discovered with a thoroughness and ferocity scarcely exceeded in modern times. Scenes such as the execution of Atahualpa, King of the Incas by Francisco Pizarro in 1532 (12), were hardly offset by the dawning awareness in Europe of the cultural as well as mineral wealth of the Americas; the Aztec sacrificial knife which Hernando Cortes gave to the Emperor Charles V was only part of a treasure given by Montezuma to the Spaniards (13). A by-product of Sir Martin Frobisher's unsuccessful attempts to discover a north-west passage to the Pacific via Canada was his encounter in 1577 with the Eskimos of Greenland (14). John White accompanied Sir Walter Raleigh to North Carolina in 1585, and his studies of Indians and their village of

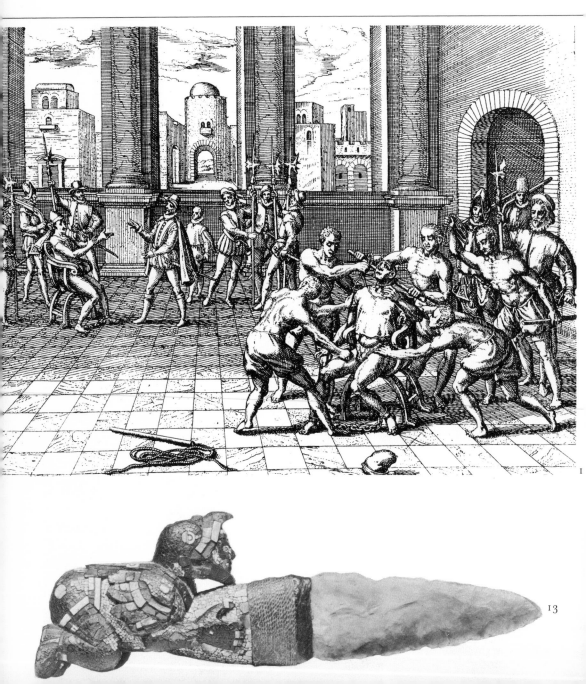

I

13

Secoton on the Pamlico River rank amongst the earliest surviving ethnographic records, and made a lasting impression upon White's contemporaries (15). Later, the exploration of Africa also led to useful observations of the native population. In 1705 Peter Kolb, a schoolmaster of Ansbach in Germany, compiled a study of the everyday life of the Hottentots of the Cape Province (16). However, with Kolb's illustrations and such engravings as this eighteenth century picture of Malabar natives (17) there is a conscious over-enobling of savage features. Likewise, the artists who accompanied Cook on his voyages could not bring themselves to paint precisely what they saw. William Hodges' painting of the monolithic statues of Easter Island is a typical landscape of the Romantic age (page 43), which owes more to the ideals of Jean-Jacques Rousseau than to the realities of discovery.

16

17

THE THEORY OF EVOLUTION. At the same time as the development of scientific geology, the principles of evolutionary sequences were also being tried out. In 1849, Sir John Evans traced the development of Iron Age British coinage from fourth century B.C. Greek prototypes (18). The culmination of such work was the full theory of natural selection and evolution presented by Charles Darwin (19). It was Darwin's observations on his voyage round the world in H.M.S. *Beagle* between 1831–36, including the unique flora and fauna of the isolated Galapagos Islands, which guided his first thoughts on "the transmutation of species". Darwin's notes on such animals as "the disgusting clumsy lizards", the marine iguanas (20), brought home to him for the first time the key fact of the gradual development of living things. In 1859 Darwin published the first edition of *The Origin of Species*, which was an immediate best-seller (21). Publication, however, was followed by wide-

18

19   20

spread rejection. A belief in natural selection was considered contrary to a belief in the Almighty's role in the creation of man. The similarity between man and monkey, widely lampooned by Darwin's critics as in this 1861 *Punch* cartoon (22), had certainly been observed before as shown by J. B. Robinet in his *Considérations philosophiques de la graduation naturelle* of 1768 (23), though Charles Lyell wrote to Darwin that he could not "go the whole orang"! Even more damaging were the petty jealousies of Sir Richard Owen, the British Museum palaeontologist, who had initially helped Darwin identify *Megatharium*, the extinct South American giant sloth. Owen is shown here riding a megatharium skeleton (24). Undeterred by these attacks, Darwin went on to write his *Descent of Man* (1871), even though his hypothesis of an ape-like ancestor of man was based on an almost complete lack of direct fossil evidence.

21

23

24

MONKEYANA.

22

AM. I
A
MAN AND
A
BROTHER?

HAND AXES AND GRAVELS. Strange pointed objects of flint had been found in European gravel pits since the Middle Ages, but they were dismissed as the tips of lightning bolts and other fanciful phenomena. In 1797, John Frere published a short note in the journal *Archaeologia*, describing stone objects which he recognized as having been humanly made artefacts, probably weapons of war (25). These had been found in a gravel pit at Hoxne in Suffolk together with bones of giant extinct animals. Frere had in fact discovered what we now call "hand axes" but his discovery went unnoticed for fifty years, because influential geologists of the time, for example Dean William Buckland (1784–1856) (27), were firmly opposed to any idea that man's antiquity was very great. It was left to a customs officer from Abbeville in northern France, Jacques Boucher de Perthes (26), to make the fundamental discovery of

25

26

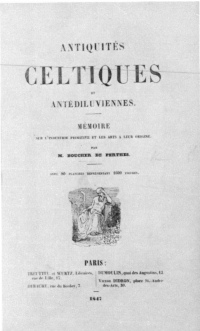

human artefacts associated with extinct animal bones in terraces of the River Somme which geologists agreed were of high antiquity, and immensely older than the chronology laid down in Genesis. Boucher de Perthes published his results in 1847 in a book entitled *Antiquités Celtiques et Antédiluviennes* (28). He had been working in quarries near Abbeville, particularly at St Acheul-les-Amiens, which are still being investigated (31), and which

gave the name "Acheulian" to one of the earliest periods of human prehistory. He found numerous hand-axes, two being shown (29, 30) with his own handwritten labels on them, the one above being particularly interesting in that it was given by Perthes in 1861 to H. Christy, the co-discoverer of the basic Middle and Upper Palaeolithic sequence in the Dordogne Caves of south-west France.

CAVE MAN. During the 1860's, Edward E. Lartet and H. Christy began systematic investigations of cave deposits such as Font-de-Gaume, near the small village of Les Eyzies, in the Dordogne region of south-west France (32). This pioneering work, followed by the classification of the excavated stone implements by Gabrielle de Mortillet, laid the foundation for our understanding of the European Old Stone Age or Middle and Upper Palaeolithic cultural succession (see Table III on p. 123). Many of the names which we now give to phases within the Stone Age, such as Mousterian, Aurignacian, Solutrean and Magdalenian, are derived from the names of caves in the Dordogne where they were first discovered. Early excavations were relatively crude, as shown in a simple drawing of the section at Aurignac published in 1879 (33). Cave exploration was both a scholarly and a gentlemanly pursuit, as in a group photograph taken outside the cave of Le Tuc d'Audoubert (35) with the

32

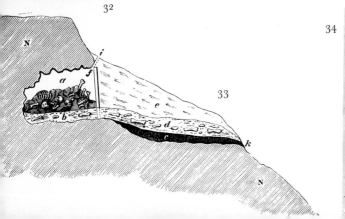

33

34

famous archaeologist Edouard Cartailhac seated in the punt wearing a beret. During early investigations, pieces of bone with delicate engravings on them had been discovered, but belief in their authenticity, as the art of Stone Age man, was long delayed partly because of pre-conceptions about the primitive mental state of savages. Magnificent cave paintings were discovered in the cave of Altamira in 1879, but it was not until the turn of the century that they, and others stylistically similar to them, were accepted by careful authorities such as Cartailhac. Since then about a hundred decorated caves have been found, including this polychrome deer at Font-de-Gaume (34), and the famous "sorcerer" of Trois Frères (36) both shown here according to the Abbé Breuil's original sketches. The entrance to the cave is shown in (37) at the time of its discovery, with Madame L. Begouen, the co-discoverer.

36   37

THE THREE AGES SYSTEM. Many would regard Darwin's evolutionary theories as a key point in the development of archaeological method. In fact, the concept of a sequence of past ages or technological stages, first conceived by the ancient Greeks, was finally worked out by Scandinavian historians and archaeologists half-a-century before Darwin's first major publication. Two lasting features of the work of these scholars were the promulgation of the world's first modern laws for the preservation and protection of ancient monuments, and the setting up of a successive classification of stone, bronze and iron. An important figure was C. J. Thomsen, appointed in 1816 as first curator of the Danish Royal Collections, later to become the Danish National Museum. From the beginning, Thomsen was concerned with the systematic organization of the collections according to the "three ages", as can be

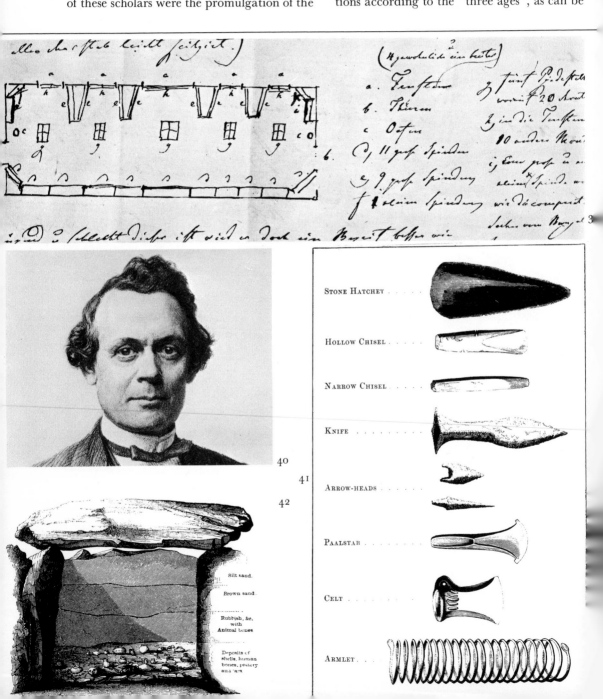

STONE HATCHET

HOLLOW CHISEL

NARROW CHISEL

KNIFE

ARROW-HEADS

PAALSTAB

CELT

ARMLET

Silt sand.

Brown sand.

Rubbish, &c. with Animal bones

Deposits of shells, human bones, pottery and ars

40

41

42

seen from his notes and plans for the new location of the National Museum in 1855 (38). Thomsen also realized the importance of public education, as is indicated by a sketch of a guide lecture of 1846 in the museum in the old royal palace at Christiansborg (39). Another Danish pioneer was J. J. A. Worsaae. He succeeded Thomsen as director of the National Museum; indeed, in many ways Worsaae has a fair claim to being the world's first professional archaeologist (40). Worsaae's *Danmarks Oldtid* (1843), published in English as *The Primeval Antiquities of Denmark* (41), was not only concerned with the chronological ordering of artefacts on the basis of their shape and the material of which they were made. It also described the stratigraphic excavation and careful recording of ancient coastal middens or rubbish dumps, peat-bog deposits, and tumuli or burial mounds (42).

CHAPTER TWO

ARCHAEOLOGICAL EVIDENCE

EVEN TODAY in a time when archaeology has entered its scientific age, there are still those who see archaeologists as being divided into two groups. There are the "dirt archaeologists", who literally dig for evidence and are considered by some to be a distinctly lesser form of life, and those who study ancient art rather than artefacts and never get a grain of earth under their fingernails or sully their minds with anything other than objects of the very highest quality. This view is really a direct outcome of those first enquiries into the classical past which we commented on in the last chapter. Johann Winckelmann, the early eighteenth century pioneering scholar of classical studies, was not so much "the father of archaeology" (as he has often been termed) as the father of art-history. But it is rare for archaeologists actually to stumble across "objects of the very highest quality", however defined. Indeed, much more commonly, such discoveries have been the outcome of pure chance; we must admit that the basic studies of the archaeologist are concerned more often with potsherds and, at the best, ill-defined ruins, than with whole Grecian urns and cities half as old as time.

Archaeological evidence is of necessity fragmentary. We can excavate a neolithic pottery figurine and compare its style of manufacture with that of other known figurines, but we cannot excavate the thoughts in the mind of its maker. Much archaeology is necessarily the archaeology of the dead; frequently we can excavate the graves of the wealthy few, but we still know next to nothing of the past's poor. Observations on chance discoveries have a long history; we have already made brief reference to prehistoric man as excavator; a Chinese court historian of the second century B.C. located the ancient Bronze Age city of Anyang. The opening in 1653 at Tournai (now in Belgium) in France of the tomb of Childeric, first King of the Franks who died in A.D. 481, was faithfully recorded and fortunately published with illustrations two years later by a local physician-turned-antiquary. The grave goods were stolen in Paris in 1831 never to be recovered—though not before Napoleon had incorporated details of Childeric's insignia in his own coronation robes. The theft of Childeric's last effects is a reminder that archaeological excavation is itself destructive. Unlike a scientific experiment, with which excavation has sometimes been compared, one can never repeat the exact conditions of a "dig". All too frequently, excavations have resembled the rape rather than the resurrection of the past; too many sites have been dug, in the words of Sir Mortimer Wheeler, "like sacks of potatoes".

No excavation should ever be undertaken without first asking oneself what questions it will answer. Interpretation of the results of excavation should provide answers to the four basic "W's" of archaeology, "what is it?", "when was it?"

"whose was it?", and "why was it?".

Excavation is not of course the only way of obtaining basic archaeological evidence. After the actual surgery of digging, the desire to wrest from the soil the maximum of information leads to the analysis of finds by every available scientific method. Bronze and copper implements are examined by a metallurgist to ascertain not only their method of manufacture but also the possible source of the ore from which they were fashioned. If conditions are favourable, the botanist can identify not only the ancient history of plant life but, in the case of corpses preserved by the tanning action of peat bogs, what was the actual last meal eaten. It was a by-product of research on the first atomic bombs, the discovery of the radio-active isotopes of carbon as absorbed by all living matter, which made possible the estimation of absolute dates from the remains of carbon in man, his food, and his artefacts.

The scientific approach to archaeology has a long history. Thomas Jefferson, third president of the United States, is famous for many things but is not generally acknowledged as one of archaeology's first scientific field workers. In 1784 he excavated an Indian burial mound in his native Virginia, making observations on the stratigraphy and nature of the burials worthy if not better than those of many later field workers. Strangely enough America has often been,

as far as archaeology is concerned, the home of good theory and bad practice. Four years after Jefferson's pioneering dig, on the other side of the world, Captain Arthur Phillip, first governor of the new colony of New South Wales, was examining coastal middens on the shores of Botany Bay and making reasonable if incorrect pronouncements, probably on the basis of his experience of the Bronze Age tumuli of the southern English downlands.

In 1880, Lieutenant-General Augustus Lane-Fox left behind him the Indian army and a pioneering typological study of fire-arms developed on the best evolutionary principles and, as General Pitt-Rivers, retired to an inheritance of 29,000 Dorset acres. There, with true military precision and the principles of "Strata" Smith, the General enthusiastically devoted himself to the investigation of Neolithic and Bronze Age burial mounds, Iron Age farmsteads and Roman villas. All this was a far cry from the contemporary and fashionable art of tomb robbing and, as much as anyone in England, Pitt-Rivers dealt a death-blow to that overriding concern with taste and aesthetics which had bedevilled much of antiquarian thought since the Renaissance.

In the following pages we examine some examples of the methods and materials of modern archaeology, particularly with reference to man's most distant past.

ARCHAEOLOGY, HISTORY, AND SURVIVAL.
Archaeology is basically a series of techniques designed to reconstruct the past from material remains. But this does not mean that archaeology can ever present a total reconstruction of the past. For example, though much has been recovered as the result of the careful excavation of a pre-European Maori *pa* or fortified settlement at Kauri Point, in the Bay of Plenty, New Zealand (43), Sydney Parkinson's sketch of another *pa* in the Bay of Islands, made during James Cook's first voyage of discovery (44), gives us much more detail than can ever be recovered with certainty by the archaeologist's trowel. Sometimes the encroaching effects of nature can literally bury the knowledge of ancient cultures for centuries. The rediscovery and recording by the

43 44

4

45

Englishman Alfred Maudslay of Maya sites such as Tikal (45) in the Guatemalan jungle started the modern study of Middle American archaeology. The sealing of the tomb of the Pharaoh Tut-ankh-amen for more than 3,300 years preserved most of its contents perfectly until its opening in 1922 (46). Water can destroy priceless historical and archaeological evidence—witness the disastrous Florence floods of 1968. But water can also preserve. Extensive drainage works in Albania revealed unique wooden structures of a Copper Age settlement of *c.* 3000–2000 B.C. (47). Extreme cold can also prevent decay. The wood-lined chambers of the Pazyryk burial mounds in Soviet Central Asia acted as a deep freeze for an embalmed and tatooed chieftain of the fifth century B.C. (48).

47

48

ARCHAEOLOGY FROM THE EARTH. Excavation is the archaeologist's basic source of raw material. Scenes like the "Ruins discovered at the Corner of Whitecomb Street near Charing Cross" from the *Gentleman's Magazine* of 1822 (49) still take place today. A detail of the excavation of an Indian burial mound forms part of a panorama of the Mississippi valley painted in 1850 and shows an early use of the principles of stratigraphy (50). Modern large-scale excavations involve the laying out of a rectangular grid, as can be seen from this view of the recent uncovering of a Roman palace at Fishbourne in Sussex (51). Special conditions demand special excavation techniques. In 1957, Danish archaeologists discovered a boom made of five Viking ships. To recover the wrecks, it was necessary to pump out the water and record every fragment of wood before beginning the long process of recon-

49

50

struction (page 44). Less than a century ago, archaeologists could rely only on the presence of historically dated objects, or on historic links, to suggest dates for their excavations. Recently, however, science has come to their aid with radiocarbon dating techniques, which measure the decaying proportion of a radio-active isotope of carbon (C 14) in samples of organic matter. This method will date samples up to 60,000 years old (52). Unfortu- nately, owing to fluctuations in the amount of C 14 in the atmosphere, radiocarbon dates often differ considerably from calendar dates. A comparison of radiocarbon dates and tree ring counts established by examining timbers of increasing antiquity such as the long living Californian bristlecone pine (53) suggests that many radiocarbon dates may be younger than "real" dates by several centuries.

53

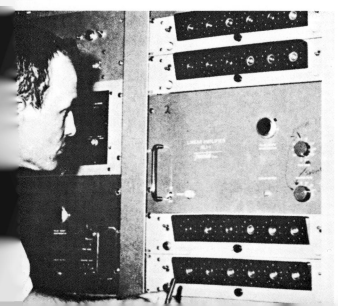

STONE TOOLS. When a fine grained, hard material such as glass or flint is struck by a hammer stone, a sharp edged flake is detached (54). Each of these flakes has certain characteristics such as a bulb of percussion, ripple marks on the same surface as the bulb, and the scars of previously detached flakes on the dorsal or reverse surface (55). These enable the archaeologist to study the way they were made. A flake may be used without further treatment as a cutting instrument, and some glass flakes are as sharp as a surgeon's scalpel. Often, however, ancient stone workers preferred to modify the edges of these flakes to make a variety of specialized tools such as scrapers, barbs for arrows, and spear points. Some of these were manufactured by pressing further flakes off the parent flake with a pointed wooden or bone lever. Some pressure flaked points are among the most beautiful

stone tools ever made, as are two fine hafted spear points from the Kimberley Mountains in north western Australia (page 45), one made from chert, and the other from green bottle glass collected by Aborigines from European bottle dumps. From the other side of the world, and 4,000 years earlier, is a Neolithic flint dagger from Denmark (56). For use, stone tools were often hafted, as is this Australian stone adze, used to manufacture a spear-thrower (57). Because of the virtual indestructibility of stone tools, they form the great bulk of man's artefacts which have survived from the earliest periods of his development, which we therefore call the "Stone Age". To gain some insight into the stone technology of ancient man, archaeologists such as Léon Coutier have studied the manufacture and the use made by modern hunters of stone tools, as well as trying actually to make tools.

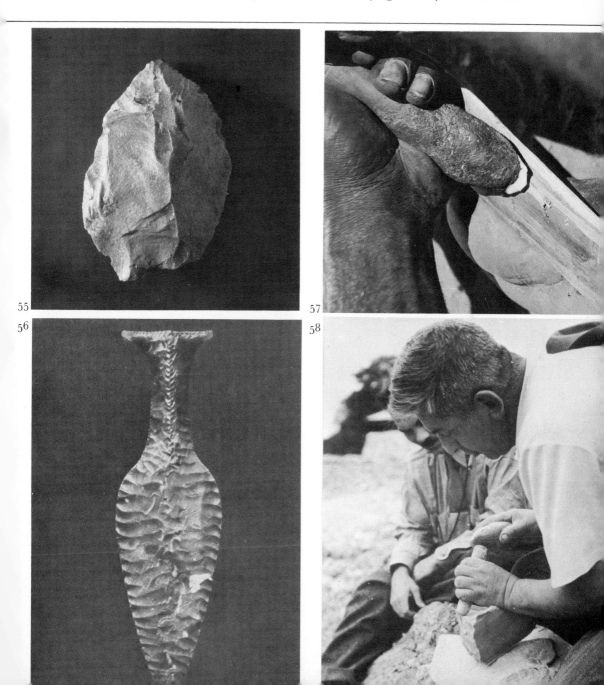

55

56

57

58

ECONOMIC RECONSTRUCTIONS. Recently, archaeologists have become increasingly interested in the economic bases of prehistoric societies, in particular diet, size and seasonal movements of local groups, trade, and the impact of man on his environment. To investigate these, many exciting avenues of research have been developed. The debris of food dumps made up of bones and shells, is now the subject of intensive analyses. At Galatea Bay in New Zealand, a prehistoric Maori shell midden was excavated (59), and the numbers and proportions of shell-fish, fish, and even dogs and humans which were eaten on the site were calculated (60). With the aid of measurements on modern samples, the meat diet of the prehistoric inhabitants was reconstructed. Prehistoric vegetable diets are difficult to analyse because most of the evidence decays rapidly, but occasionally lucky discoveries are made. A spikelet of wheat was accidentally pressed into the soft clay of a pot

59

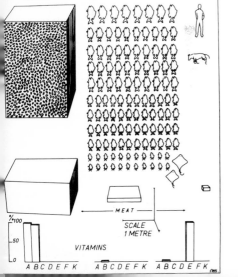

60

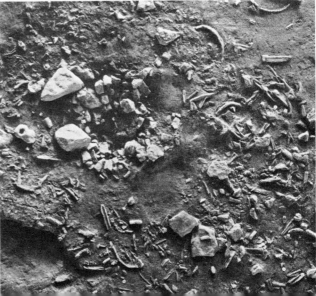

63

before it was fired about 6,000 years ago at the site of Jarmo (61). Comparison with modern species of wild wheat (62) has helped the study of the development of cereal crops. Modern excavations are planned to reveal the structures of ancient settlements, rather than to produce a mere sequence of tool types as was so often the case earlier this century. At Pincevant, France, we see part of a Magdalenian house with a hearth and animal bones strewn around it (63). Ethnographic studies of living societies often provide invaluable insights into parallel prehistoric situations. For example, a 1970 wet season camp in Arnhem Land, Australia, consisted of a few houses (64) with stone hearths, implements and food debris, much the same as in Palaeolithic sites. But here we see the whole houses, know precisely the number of people who lived in each, and can analyse the role of this camp within the total economy.

61

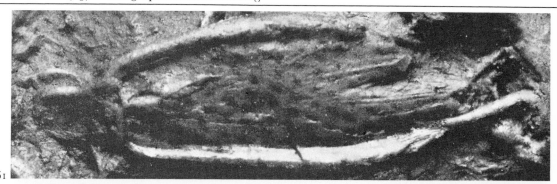

62

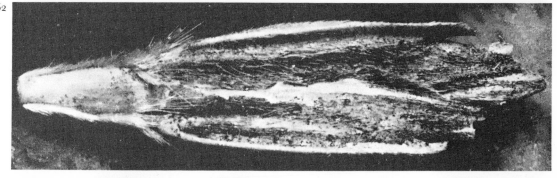

64

CHAPTER THREE
THE PRIMATES

THE EARTH is at least 4,000 million years old and the first primates appeared about 70 million years ago, but man himself is not much more than two million years old.

The modern classification of the primates consists of two main subdivisions or "suborders", the *Anthropoidea* (man and the apes) and the lower primates or *Prosimii*, which include the lemurs, tarsiers and the bush-baby. All primates except for man are adapted to living in trees. The prosimians are small in size and brain capacity compared to other primates, and it seems probable that they reflect a stage of development prior to that of the *Anthropoidea*. The first fossil primates —known only from their teeth—date geologically to the Cretaceous period some 70 million years ago. The first skeletons of what seem basically to have been ground-living quadrupeds date to the Palaeocene (some 60 million years ago). During the ensuing Eocene, the first signs of adaptation to a tree-based existence appear among the large number of primates which are known from the fossil deposits from this period. Among these early primates, the vertical posture adapted to leaping from branch to branch has become the norm, to judge from examination of the sixty or so fossil skeletons scattered throughout the world. Today the higher primates are divided into New and Old World monkeys on the one hand, and apes and man on the other. The two main groups of monkeys probably developed

from quite distinct prosimian ancestors. Though ape fossils are known from the Miocene forest beds (20 million years ago), Old World monkeys are not well authenticated before the Pliocene (after 10 million years ago).

Among the hominoids, the man-like primates, it is common now to distinguish three families: the gibbons, who apparently mark the last stage of a very long evolutionary series, the great apes, and man. The attachment of mother to offspring, food-sharing, the ability for tool-making and even aesthetic ability and comprehension are all features of the greater apes and not solely the characteristics of man. As to origins, although the first fossil ape, *Dryopithecus fontani*, discovered in Miocene deposits in France, was known to Darwin, the exact ancestry of modern apes is not easily deduced from fossil records. The Dryopithicines originated in Africa during the Oligocene (40 to 30 million years ago), and some migrated to India and Europe. But though they probably included ancestors of living apes, they did not include those of man himself. Actual "hominids", or the direct ancestors of man evolved from a common ancestor to the chimpanzee and the gorilla more than 14 million years ago. From the same Punjab region in India which has provided remains of Dryopithecus come the fragments of the jaw of what seems to have been an ancestor of the later well-documented Pleistocene hominids. *Ramapithe-*

cus, as this Indian find is called, has a human-like palate and smaller teeth than those of other fossil or modern apes; this small size is very important in the diagnosis of human dentition.

With the onset of the Pleistocene, around two million years ago, the picture becomes even more complex. The first Pleistocene hominid to have been identified was the child whose skull was discovered at Taung in Botswana, South Africa, in 1924. The Taung skull is one of the small brained human-jawed *Australopithecus africanus*, who may date back geologically to the Pliocene. Several other fossil skulls of the *Australopithecus* type have been found in South Africa, the most prolific site being Sterkfontein in the Transvaal. The average cranial capacity of such fossils is 485 *cc.*, or about that of the modern gorilla. Tools were found when a slightly younger and larger fossil type was discovered at Swartkrans near Sterkfontein. This species was named by its discoverer *Paranthropus robustus*, but it may also be an Australopithecine. The total evidence from the South African sites indicates that *Australopithecus* was an open woodland and grasslands hunter, was bi-pedal and could make simple tools. Certainly, he was quite unlike modern apes.

In East Africa, the fossil hominids from the ancient lake sediments of the Olduvai Gorge of Tanzania have been painstak-ingly uncovered over the past forty years by Mary and Louis Leakey. The basal beds at Olduvai date approximately to the transition between the Pliocene and the Pleistocene, just less than two million years ago. Of two species represented at Olduvai, the more robust, *Zinjanthropus boisei*, suggests to some an identity with the more southerly *Paranthropus* —in other words it belongs to the Australopithecines. The second more slender Olduvai species, now named *Homo habilis*, is an early Pleistocene small-brained bipedal crea-ture, which has been compared with Australopithecines from Sterkfontein and other sites. The designation "Homo" indi-cates that the Leakeys considered *Homo habilis* to be an ancestor of modern man. Most recently there is evidence from Kenya of the undoubted association of tools with a slender Australopithecine type of $2\frac{1}{2}$ million years ago, well within the Pliocene. The Olduvai living sites include evidence of a rough shelter and the refuse from the slaughter of large animals. This evidence suggests that the Olduvai hominids were capable of organ-izing cooperative hunting bands, unlike the present higher apes who, when in groups, have strict patterns of dominance. *Homo habilis*, however, could hardly be regarded as having been very intelligent; it is unlikely, for example, that speech was highly developed, if indeed it was devel-oped at all.

THE PRIMATES. The study of certain primates can help the anthropologist to reconstruct the ancestry of man. In contrast, the most primitive primates, the "prosimians", like the ring-tailed lemur (65), are quadrupeds, and have large forward-set eyes. The New World marmoset (66) is the smallest of the living monkeys, and it would appear that its ancestors split off from the other primates before the evolution of the Old World apes (67). One chief difference between apes and monkeys is the apes' greater freedom of movement in their fore-limbs. The gibbon often walks upright along branches, and even descends to the ground on two feet (68). The timid giant, the gorilla, is the largest of the apes (69); he propels himself on all fours, and spends most of his life on the ground rather than in trees. The primates can also help us to understand human behaviour. The savannah living

65 66
67

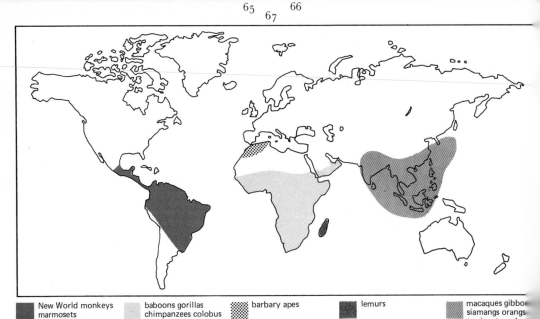

| New World monkeys marmosets spider and howler monkeys | baboons gorillas chimpanzees colobus galagos lorises cercopithecus | barbary apes | lemurs | macaques gibbons siamangs orangs tarsiers tree-shrews lorises langurs |

baboons of Kenya live within defined territories and are naturally aggressive; all the members of a troop are subject to the dominant males. When on the move, these males take up a position flanking the females and the young, and subordinate males are placed at the head and the rear (page 45). Mothers with infants are highly prized and protected (70). The ability to walk on two legs, freeing the fore-limbs for new learned skills, is probably connected with the development of tool-making ability, an ability the higher apes in fact share with man. Even more surprising is the observation of apparent artistic skills and aesthetic appreciation amongst chimpanzees, one of whom Congo of the London Zoo, in three years painted nearly 400 pictures. Over a period of time changes in style and even technique could be observed (71).

68   69   70   71

ETHOLOGY. It is easy to show superficial similarities in expression and gesture between man and his close primate relatives (72 and 73), and these give us amusement because we see in them a parody of human actions. The biological study of behaviour or "ethology" has gained importance in recent years. Early work on groups of birds, for example that of Conrad Lorenz with snow geese (74), showed the existence of social behaviour previously believed to have belonged exclusively to man. Thus a bond between mother and infant, formation and maintenance of social hierarchies, and territoriality, have all been shown to exist in a wide range of animal societies including those of man. An angry man (75) will open his mouth baring his teeth, his eye brows will glower, and he will often bellow or roar. Similar reactions can be seen in baboons, the one in (76) showing the

72

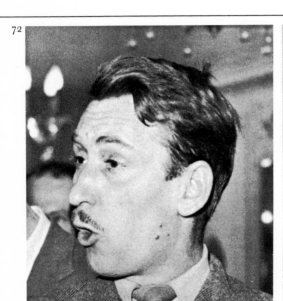

73

74

opposite reaction to danger, namely fear. A comparative study of aspects of animal behaviour may well give insights into the social behaviour of early man who, before he had tools, must have been subject to many of the same ecological conditions as modern baboons. In addition to the core of inherited social and emotional behaviour which we share with other animals, and in particular with the other primates, man has also developed "culture", expressed both in material terms such as tools, and in social and abstract terms such as language and intellect. It was culture which gave him a decisive evolutionary advantage over his competitors in the late Pliocene, and it may well be culture which will curb some aspects of his inherited behaviour which now threaten his very existence.

75 76

39

THE OLDUVAI GORGE in Tanzania (page 46) was formed by a river cutting through a series of sediments laid down during the Pleistocene in and around the shores of a lake. Drs. Mary and Louis Leakey discovered that the various beds contained bones of hominids and a range of stone tools dating back one and three-quarter million years. The first hominid remains named by Leakey *Zinjanthropus boisei* or "Nutcracker man", were found alongside broken animal bones and stone tools (77). More recently, a second smaller type, *Homo habilis*, has also been recognized. One of the hominid species at Olduvai, probably Homo *habilis*, was certainly associated with extensive tool-making, of which the simple "pebble-choppers" were only the largest forms (78). Higher up the Olduvai beds, one can follow the evolution of the first true hand-axes, (79) and (80).

77

79

80

78

"Earthly Paradise"—a painting by Hieronymous Bosch (*c.* 1450–1516) symbolizing the haunting fear of hell fire and witchcraft in a world peopled by the unknown (from page 10)

A European vision of the Pacific "Easter Island"—
a painting by William Hodges (1774–1797)
(from page 15)

Opposite A medieval view of the Ancient Near East.
The building of the Tower of Babel from a French
book of hours (from page 10)

Opposite Salvage archaeology. The
Viking ships of Roskilde (from page 28)

Right Two hafted spear points from the
Kimberleys in north western Australia
(from page 31)
Below Baboons on the move with the
dominant males flanking the females
and young, and subordinate males at
the head and rear (from page 37)

The Olduvai Gorge, Tanzania (from page 40)

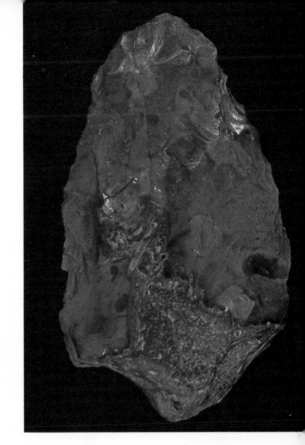

Right The most important implement developed during the Middle Pleistocene was the "hand-axe" (from page 62)

Below At Mungo, New South Wales, Australia, between 25,000 and 30,000 years ago, people lived on sand dunes by the shores of large lakes which have since dried up (from page 90)

Reindeer herds like these from Swedish Lapland
roamed over France and in central Europe during the
Last Ice Age, a period which commenced
approximately 30,000 years, and lasted until 10,000
years ago (from page 77)

The caves at Lascaux in south-western France
demonstrate the variety of style and motif found in
Upper Palaeolithic art (from page 88)

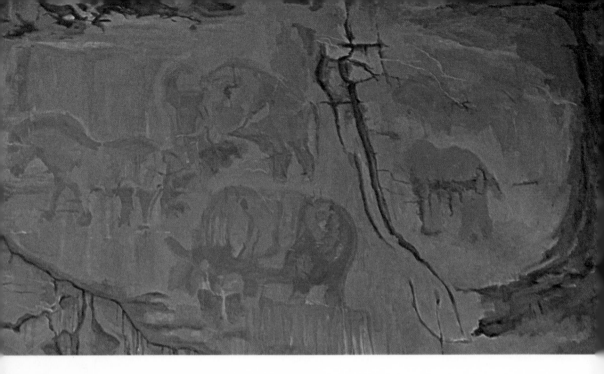

Above Palaeolithic drawings discovered in the Kapovaya Cave in the Urals (from page 88)
Left An Aboriginal painting from Arnhem Land in northern Australia. Many caves are dominated by strange human figures with elaborate head-dresses (from page 95)

Opposite above A single-piece ard from Turkey, a scratch plough evolved in *c.* 4000 B.C. and still used extensively in Asia and the Middle East today (from page 99)

Opposite below "Sioux at Fort Pierre", an engraving by Charles Bodmer, illustrating a Redskin mounted band of the great days of the Wild West (from page 101)

The Inca citadel at Macchu Picchu, Peru, a cultural
development of large ceremonial structures (from
page 107)

Opposite The Mesolithic "Maglemosean" ("big bog")
culture produced attractive carvings of animals and
abstract forms from Baltic amber (from page 105)

On the west coast of Tasmania, rocks such as these at
Mount Cameron West were carved about 2,000 years ago
by the Aborigines (from page 113)

In the Amazon, small groups of plant gatherers and
hunters live on the periphery of horticultural peoples
(from page 116)

The houses of the people of the Oriomo Plateau in southern
Papua are made from a framework of forked poles and
roofed with bark (from page 117)

THE FIRST APE-MEN. Some forty years ago, hominid remains were found in limestone caves in South Africa, and assigned to the genus *Australopithecus*, or "Southern ape-man". In 1936, Dr. Robert Broom discovered a skull imbedded in a limestone cave at Sterkfontein in the Transvaal (81). Although difficult to date, this and several other finds from Sterkfontein (82, 83), may be as old as 2½ million years. Another fossil site dating to the end of the early Pleistocene was discovered at Swartkrans, again in the Transvaal. The massive appearance of the Swartkrans skulls resulted in the name of *Australopithecus* (or *Paranthropus*) *robustus* (84). The Australopithecines were small-brained, bipedal creatures, with massive ape-like jaws, who lived in high open country, and probably hunted in groups for other free-ranging animals and sheltered in caves (85).

84

85

81

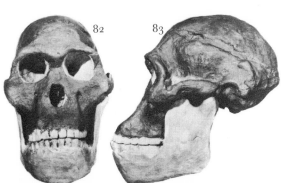

82 83

CHAPTER FOUR

MAN BECOMES HUMAN

DURING THE EARLY and Middle Pleistocene, the genus *Homo* evolved rapidly and, by about half a million years ago, his physical form and his capacity for the manufacture of tools had changed radically from his early Pleistocene forebears. The first Middle Pleistocene human skull was discovered in 1891 on the banks of the Solo River, Java, by Eugene Dubois, who named it *Pithecanthropus erectus*, or "erect ape-man". Similar skulls found in the Chou-k'ou-tien Cave near Peking were named *Sinanthropus pekinensis*. It is now clear that these and other related types can all be grouped into one species of the genus *Homo*, and called *Homo erectus*. *Homo erectus* skulls are characterized by prominent brow ridges, flat sloping foreheads, constrictions behind the eye-sockets, and a protruding face. His brain capacity is estimated to have been 900 to 1000 *cc*, a marked increase on earlier hominids. *Erectus* types had a wide distribution throughout the Old World, being found in China and Indonesia in the East, South and Central Africa in the West, and as far north as Central Europe.

He was capable of manufacturing standardized stone tools, and excavations of his living sites show him to have been an accomplished hunter. The most important stone tool to be developed during this period was the "hand-axe", the first discoveries of which we have already discussed. This type of axe was originally derived from advanced pebble tools and

the first hand-axes, half a million years old, were crudely flaked: only about a dozen separate blows with a hammer stone were needed to manufacture each one. They became progressively more refined until, by about 250,000 years ago, the classic Acheulian hand-axes were being made. Hand axes have been found throughout Africa, Europe as far north as England and Hungary, the Levant and India, but they are rare or absent east of Burma where contemporary industries are characterized by "choppers" made from pebbles and larger flake tools. This indicates the existence of at least two major cultural provinces during late Middle Pleistocene times (See Table II on p. 123).

Settlement sites have been found as far apart as Chou-k'ou-tien, Spain, Terra Amata in France and Olorgesailie in central Africa. These show that Middle Pleistocene man successfully hunted a wide variety of large game including rhinoceros, elephant, wild pig and deer. He was capable of using fire, and probably lived and foraged in small bands.

The Swanscombe and Steinheim skulls of western Europe dating back about 250,000 years are probably early *Homo sapiens*, showing the gradual development of a *sapiens* stock out of a late Middle Pleistocene *Homo erectus* gene pool. Early *Homo sapiens* showed considerable physical variation, with divisions into several well distinguished sub-groups or races, such as those of Neanderthal, Rhodesia and Solo men. These were formerly classified into different species from our own, but they are now seen as geographic sub-species of early *sapiens* types. Varieties of Neanderthal man, or closely related types, lived in Europe, the Middle East and Africa from about 150,000 years ago to 30,000 years ago. The more extreme forms, the so-called "classic Neanderthalers" probably represented a genetic drift in Western Europe which was then an isolated corner of the early *sapiens* world. At the same time, the direct ancestors of modern man were also evolving, and it is worth remembering that there was also a late survival of archaic *erectus* traits in several populations, for example in the Omo Valley, East Africa, and possibly in Australia.

Neanderthal men had rugged skulls, with prominent brow ridges, sloping foreheads and protruding faces, and their brain size in some cases exceeded ours. There is no truth in the popular idea of Neanderthalers as shambling, semi-human cave men. They stood upright and, seen in the flesh, they would have been short, thick set fellows.

Their stone artefacts are grouped together into what is called the Mousterian culture, which developed out of the late Acheulian period. This culture was based on the manufacture of implements from prepared cores which gave the worker much more control over the shape of the desired flakes, which were then trimmed to form curved edge knives, broad points, and steep scrapers. Small hand axes were used in some areas, and delicate bifacially worked points in others. In Europe there were several regional provinces within Mousterian industries, implying the existence of social groupings, similar to large tribes, with slightly different cultures. The Mousterians were skilled hunters, and killed bear, mammoth, deer and other game. In spite of the fact that from 70,000 to about 40,000 years ago the climate was colder than now, the Mousterians managed to extend their geographical range northwards to the Russian steppes. They buried their dead with care, sometimes with objects which may have been grave goods of some sort, implying belief or interest in life after death.

Similar events to these were taking place in Africa and in eastern Asia, and somewhere within this widespread Upper Pleistocene era of physical and cultural evolution, modern man and his culture were developing.

60 PALAEOCLIMATOLOGY. The climate of the world has changed many times in the past, and natural scientists have studied these changes by a variety of techniques (see Table I on p. 122). Evidence for cold periods or "ice ages" has come partly from a study of modern glaciers such as on the Alaska-Canada border (86), which shows deeply gouged U-shaped valleys and gravel moraines. Animals and plants respond to climatic changes, and a study of the fossil record can often give us information about past climates. This rhinoceros molar (87 and 88) from an English gravel pit dated to the Pleistocene shows that the climate then was probably warmer than now. Pollen from trees is trapped and conserved in peat bogs. Cores dug into these bogs can be analysed, and a "pollen curve" constructed showing the relative abundance of various species of trees at dif-

ferent times in the past. For example a pollen curve for western Europe during the past 12,000 years would show birch and pine trees, which thrive in cold conditions, being replaced by warmth-loving oaks and beeches. During ice ages, water is locked up in ice sheets, and the level of the sea drops. Conversely during a warmer period the sea level rises. Evidence for high sea levels in the past throughout the world have come from raised beaches and high sea caves (89). Modern studies on the isotopes of oxygen can even give absolute figures to these temperature changes. This has been done with samples taken from the 100,000 year old cave of Haua Fteah in North Africa (90). In the past, climates have also been more wet or more dry than they are today. In central Australia, there is a series of sand dune crescents which, 17,000 years ago, fringed large lakes. Now it is a semi-desert (91).

87 88

89

90 91

THE ACHEULIAN. During the Middle Pleistocene, great advances were made in stone technology. The most important implement to be developed during this period was the "hand axe" (page 47). This is a flat tool which has been flaked from both sides to give it a sharp edge. One end is pointed and the other usually curved. There is great variety in the shape of these implements; some are oval in shape and others markedly elongated (92, 93). They were manufactured from many different types of stone. Nevertheless, their shape is remarkably standardized, which shows that the worker had excellent control over his materials, and that he was working to exact specifications which probably involved aesthetic as well as purely utilitarian considerations. Hand axes were multi-purpose tools, their uses ranging from skinning animals to digging for roots. There was a steady evolution in the shape of these tools, from early crudely flaked ones over half a million years

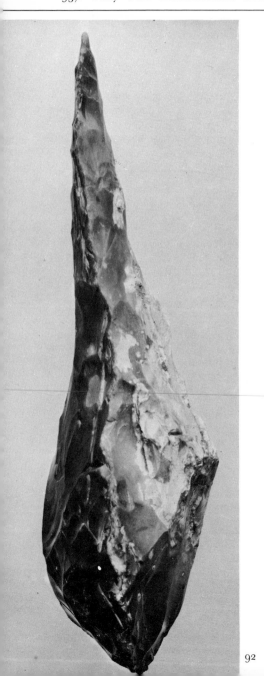

old, through to the evolved hand axes of the Acheulian period which flourished some 250,000 years ago (92) and (93); (see also Table III on p. 123). The centre for these developments was Africa. Large open Acheulian sites have been found, for example, at Orlogesailie in Kenya (94), where a working floor contained hundreds of hand axes strewn across an ancient ground surface (95). Contemporary with Acheulian sites in western Europe are others which contain mostly large flake tools; "prepared core" industries eventually replaced the Acheulean ones. The core shown in (96) is about 180,000 years old and most of its flakes have been brought together again. The tip of a wooden spear (97) from Clacton, Essex, believed to date from Acheulian times, serves to remind us that Acheulian man probably had many implements of wood, almost all of which have decayed to nothing.

94 95

96

97

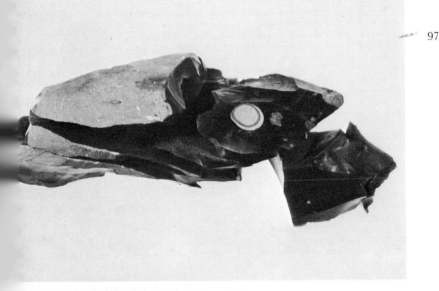

HOMO ERECTUS. In 1891, the Dutchman Eugene Dubois (98) discovered on the banks of the Solo River in Java (99) the skull which he had gone half way across the world to seek. So confident was he that he would find the link between man and apes, that he had invented a name for it—*Pithecanthropus erectus* or erect ape-man, before he had even discovered it! Java Man and similar skulls are now grouped together as *Homo erectus*. These are seen as the Middle Pleistocene human genetic stock from which Neanderthal man and other early *Homo sapiens* evolved. Near Heidelberg in Germany, a massive mandible called the Mauer jaw (100) was discovered in 1907 at the base of a deep cutting in a sand quarry; the "X" in (101) marks the presumed location of the find. The jaw is characterized

98   99

100
101

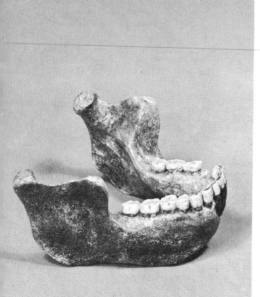

by a wide ramus or side of the mandible, large teeth and a curved deep front. *Erectus* finds have also been made in Africa and in China. The famous Peking Man from Chou-k'ou-tien is represented by several almost complete skulls. A top view (102) and a partial reconstruction of a frontal view (103) of one of these skulls shows some of the distinctive *Homo erectus* characteristics. These include a pro-

truding face, a sloping forehead and prominent brow ridges, with marked constrictions behind the forehead, which give the top of the cranium a jar-shaped profile (102). Most of these skulls date from about 500,000 years ago, but recent discoveries suggest some archaic and possibly *erectus* traits continued in some areas of the world until much more recent times.

65

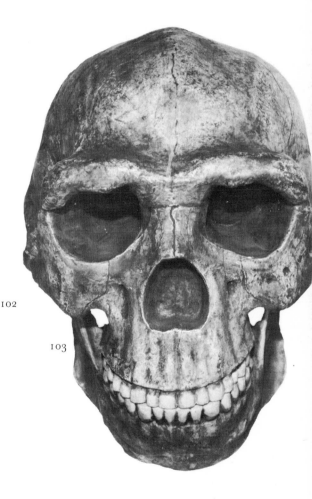

102

103

LIFE AND TIMES IN THE MIDDLE PLEISTOCENE. At the cave site of Chou-k'ou-tien (104), archaeologists have been able to reconstruct many aspects of the diet, living habits and stone technology of Peking Man, the hominid who lived in China about half a million years ago. A block of this occupation deposit (105) shows calcined bones and artefacts made from quartz. Peking Man used fire to keep himself warm and probably to cook his meat. He killed a wide variety of animals including deer, pig, rhinoceros and monkey. Judging from fractures at the base of some human skulls at the site, he may also have been a cannibal. Pebbles were flaked to form heavy chopping tools (106), and quartz flakes were bashed between hammer stones and anvils for use as chisels, resulting in characteristic bipolar flaking (107, 108). An archaeologically accurate reconstruction by Maurice

04

105

106

107

0 1

Wilson of Peking Man and his family in their cave home is shown in (109). Another important Middle Pleistocene living site is the recently discovered one at Terra Amata on the south coast of France near Nice. Here Henry de Lumley has excavated an Abbevillian or early Acheulian settlement dating back some 300,000 years. (110) shows part of the floor of one of the huts, revealing the ancient domestic debris including stone tools and a stag's antler. Large game animals were killed and eaten including rhinoceros, deer, elephant and ibex. Shell fish were collected from the nearby sea shore. In (111), we see a chipping floor in one of the huts. The clear area in the middle is where the worker sat, and in a circle around this are the flakes and cores which he chipped and discarded. Several of these can be fitted together to reconstruct the original core.

110

111

4

MOUSTERIAN CULTURE. Neanderthal man manufactured his flakes from carefully prepared cores, and was thus able to exert much more control over the shape of the flake. This could then be used for a variety of purposes with the minimum of further modification. Among the implements manufactured were broad points with wide striking platforms seen on the left hand side of (112) (two implements from the 1863 excavations of Lartet and Christy); others were small hand-axes, and side scrapers with long curved steep edges (on the right of 112), which were probably used for cutting meat or scraping hides. Bones were used as well (113), such as these metapodial stone-working anvils from La Quina, France. These industries are grouped into what is known as the Mousterian culture, which flourished in Europe, north Africa and western Asia from about 100,000 to 30,000 years ago. There was considerable regional variation throughout this area, but all the Mousterian

112 113

114 115

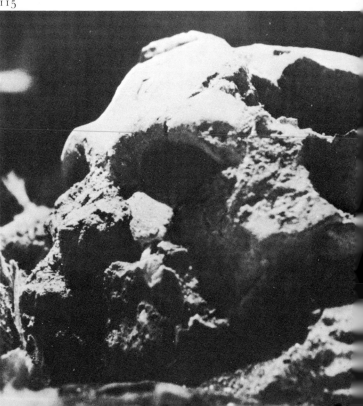

remains have certain common characteristics, and probably evolved slowly from an advanced Acheulean tradition. The Mousterians were skilled hunters, as shown by the bone debris on the floor of the Grotte du Renne at Arcy-sur-Cure (114). Their technology enabled them successfully to dispute the possession of caves with bears, sabre-tooth tigers, and lions. In Eurasia, they extended their range northwards to include the Russian steppes. At a cave near Shanidar in Iraq (116),

an old Neanderthal man (115) was killed by a slab of rock which had fallen on to him from the roof. His body was simply left where it lay; on other occasions though Neanderthal man carried out burial rites. At Teshik-Tash in Uzbekistan, a boy was buried surrounded by the frontlets of goats which were stuck into the ground in a circle around the skull (117). Here is tangible evidence of concepts of spirituality and of the mystery of death.

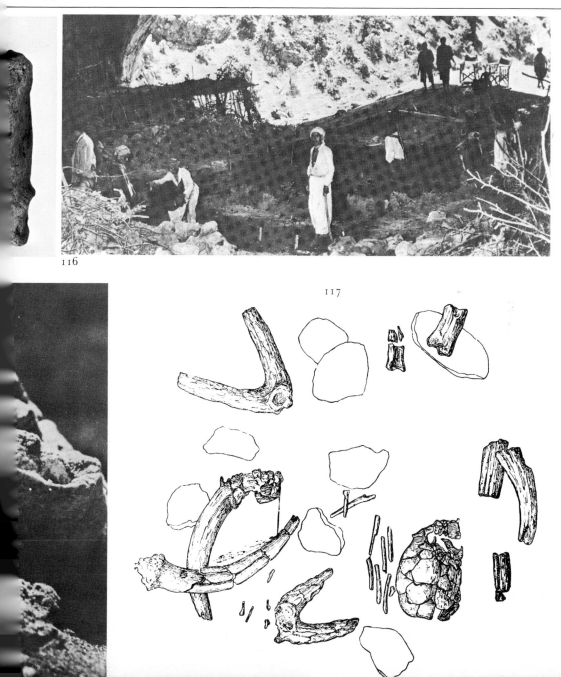

116

117

NEANDERTHAL MAN. Neanderthal Man lived in Europe, western Asia and Africa, between 150,000 and 30,000 years ago (see Table III, on p. 123). Originally classified as *Homo neanderthalensis*, he is now seen as a sub-group of *Homo sapiens*. Neanderthal men probably evolved from a general *erectus* or early *sapiens* stock, and in some places, notably western Europe, they developed certain physical characteristics which, by 50,000 years ago, gave them a distinctively different appearance from their cousins, the direct ancestors of modern man, who were developing during the same period somewhere in Asia. Competition with modern *sapiens* types between 50,000 and 30,000 years ago brought about the disappearance of Neanderthal man. A skull discovered in a Broken Hill, Rhodesia, mine (118), exemplifies the physical characteristics of Neanderthal Man. These include massive and prominent

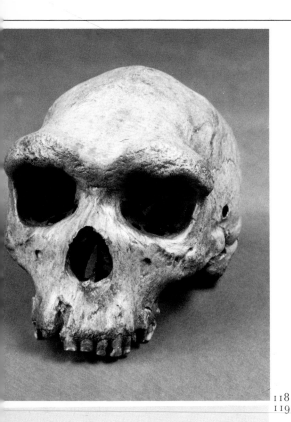

118
119

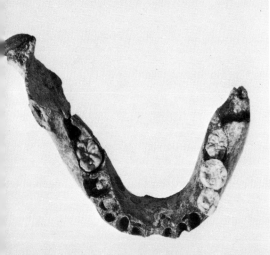

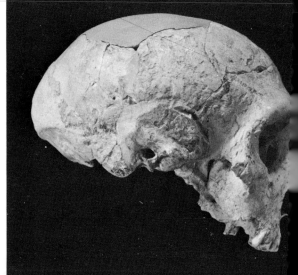

brow ridges, a sloping forehead, a long flat cranium and a protruding face. Rhodesia Man must have suffered severely from toothache, as most of his teeth have rotted away with several burst abscesses in the bone of the jaw. (120) shows how he may have looked. At a cave in Gibraltar, several Neanderthal skulls were found, including the mandible of a child (119) and the cranium of a man (121). An imaginary scene outside the Gibraltar caves during the early part of the last Ice Age, about 50,000 years ago, is shown in (122), with people dining on ibex and a bird, now extinct, called the Great Auk. These reconstructions require a disciplined scientific imagination to place the flesh on to the fossil bones. One remarkable find, a Neanderthal footprint discovered in a cave in Italy called "Grotta della Basura" (123), shows that the Neanderthal foot was broader than ours.

CHAPTER FIVE

THE EMERGENCE OF MODERN MAN

THE PREVIOUS CHAPTER discussed the evolution of *Homo sapiens* in his various genetic and cultural groups from about 250,000 to 30,000 years ago. Towards the end of this period we get the firm appearance of modern man, *Homo sapiens*, and his culture, an event which naturally has an enormous significance in our history.

In western Asia and neighbouring regions, modern man is associated with a new tradition of stone technology classified as the "Upper Palaeolithic" to distinguish it from the preceding "Middle Palaeolithic" industries such as the Mousterian. The new industries were based on the manufacture of long narrow blades, which were made by hammering the core with the aid of a sharp wooden or bone punch. From these blades, a variety of specialized tools were manufactured including long end-scrapers, high-keeled scrapers and chisel-like burins. From their first appearance, regional variants are apparent. One important division is based on the presence or absence of small elongated triangular bladelets with one margin heavily blunted, called "backed blades", which are presumed to have been hafted barbs or cutting edges for spears or knives (See Table III on p. 123).

Upper Palaeolithic industries make their first appearance in caves in the Levant and on the North African coast between 45,000 and 50,000 years ago. At first, they are interleaved in the deposits with Middle Palaeolithic industries, sug-

gesting periodic re-invasions from a key area somewhere to the east. But at Haua Fteah in Libya, from about 45,000 years B.C. onwards, a fully Upper Palaeolithic industry is permanently established. During this time, western Europe was firmly in the grip of Mousterian-type cultures. About 40,000 years ago, the carriers of Upper Palaeolithic industries began to spread into Europe from the Middle East, and reached the Atlantic seaboard just over 30,000 years ago. Whether there was a clash of men and cultures, or whether there was some fusing of the two, with absorption of Neanderthal genes into the modern *sapiens* stock, is a question of active research. Skulls of anatomically modern man have been found in France dating back about 25,000 years, and it is probable that in Europe there have been few important morphological changes since.

The classic European Upper Palaeolithic sequence was originally set up in France, where a succession of cultural phases have been named and analysed. Internal changes in fashions of artefact making within the Upper Palaeolithic tradition have been the subject of detailed studies by archaeologists. What interests us though, are some of the radical cultural innovations which modern man accomplished. The most striking is the invention of art, or at least its massive development. Even in the earliest Upper Palaeolithic levels, there are pieces of bone and ivory decorated with representations of animals and, in some cases, men and women. A unified artistic cycle which probably had a strong metaphysical content developed during 15,000 years to culminate in the great cave paintings of the Magdalenian era, some 10,000 years ago. Upper Palaeolithic people lived in large bands or even tribes, manufacturing complex huts and following herds of game animals on their seasonal migrations. Varieties of bone tools were invented. They carefully buried their dead with grave goods such as simple ornaments, and valued objects were traded over long distances.

Similar events were taking place on the other side of the world. Anatomically modern skulls have been dated to 40,000 years in Borneo and about 25,000 years in the Philippines. About this time or earlier, man had managed to cross the water barriers of the island chain to reach the Australian continent. A cremated anatomically modern female skull from Lake Mungo has been dated to be between 25,000 and 30,000 years old. Other fossil skulls from South East Australia date variously from 20,000 to 10,000 years ago or less. Although they are fully *sapiens* in type, they retain several intriguingly archaic anatomical features such as ruggedness and sloping foreheads. The Australian and south-east Asian stone industries are characterized by core-scrapers and steep-edge step-flaked scrapers, traditions which are distinctively different to contemporary ones in Western Asia and Europe. In Japan, a fully developed blade and engraving tool technology made its first appearance 20,000 years ago. In Australia edge ground axes are more than 20,000 years old, so probably is cave art, and a wide hunting, fishing and gathering economy had been developed to exploit the new continental environment.

The Americas are now known to have been colonized by man at least 20,000 years ago and, as in Australia, the final estimate may be much older than present evidence indicates. The oldest American industries consist of core tools and steep scrapers, similar in many ways to the technology of eastern Asia. In Southern and Central Africa, it is possible that older cultural traditions still had a strong influence. Late Acheulian industries survived locally until 50,000 years ago. Distinctive Upper Palaeolithic type industries may only have penetrated into this region 15,000 to 20,000 years ago, to replace a basically Middle Palaeolithic tradition.

Taking a world view, we see that the period from 50,000 to 30,000 years ago was a decisive one for man. By then he had developed physically, mentally and culturally so that we see him fully as modern man with his flexible technologies, his complex societies, his art and his ideas about mortality and nature. He had extended his geographical range to the furthest corners of the globe. From then on, the changes in his morphology have been negligible.

THE EMERGENCE OF MODERN MAN. At Swanscombe near London, parts of a human cranium have been found in deposits dating to 250,000 years ago, and are shown reassembled in (124). In spite of its high antiquity, this skull shows many "modern" morphological features, and is undoubtedly an early form of *Homo sapiens*. In caves at Mt. Carmel, Israel (125) two skulls were found which are thought to be about 40,000–30,000 years old, and share some characteristics of both Neanderthal and modern man. More clues about the emergence of modern man come from the cave of Haua Fteah (126) on the Libyan coast of North Africa, where a fully developed Upper Palaeothic industry appears at a level dated to 45,000 years ago, when Europe was still occupied by Neanderthalers. The oldest totally modern *sapiens* skull in Europe is the Cro Magnon man (127), about 25,000 years

124 125

126

old. Similar finds have been made on the other side of Asia. In Niah Cave, Borneo, a modern *Homo sapiens* skull has been excavated in a level dated to 40,000 years old. This skull is again *Homo sapiens* (128). In Australia, the cremated bones of two young women, undoubtedly *Homo sapiens*, have been found at Lake Mungo, New South Wales, dating to about 30,000 years ago (129). Skulls excavated at Kow Swamp in Victoria show archaic characteristics such as prominent brow ridges, sloping foreheads and constrictions behind the eye sockets (130) reminiscent of early *sapiens* types elsewhere, although some of these Australian specimens are as young as about 10,000 years. Whether this is a mixture of an archaic and a modern type, or an example of independent evolution is not yet known.

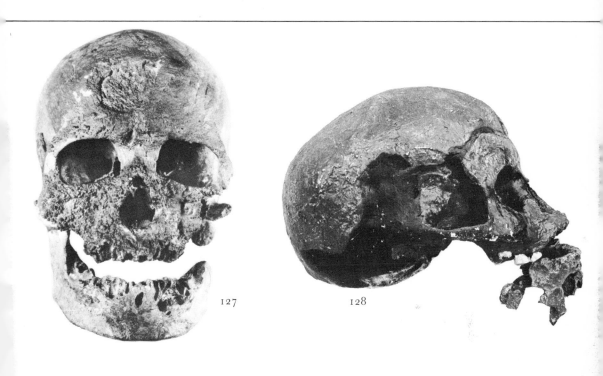

127   128

129   130

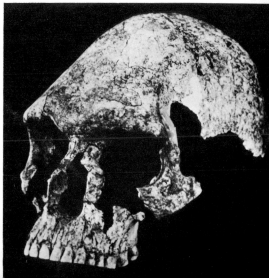

THE LAST ICE AGE. Approximately 30,000 years ago saw the onset of the main phase of the Last Ice Age which lasted until 10,000 years ago; the coldest point was reached about 18,000 to 20,000 years ago (see Table I on p. 122). This period is known as the Würm Glaciation after a small river in Austria where evidence for it was first discovered. An ice sheet from Scandinavia covered the German plains, another covered northern Britain as far south as a line from South Wales to the Wash, and the Alpine valleys contained large glaciers (131). The country south of these ice sheets consisted of cold tundra with outwash gravels and marshes which melted in summer, rather like northern Canada today (132). Southern Europe probably enjoyed a climate similar to that of modern northern Europe. Much of the European fauna was arctic, their modern descendants having retreated north-

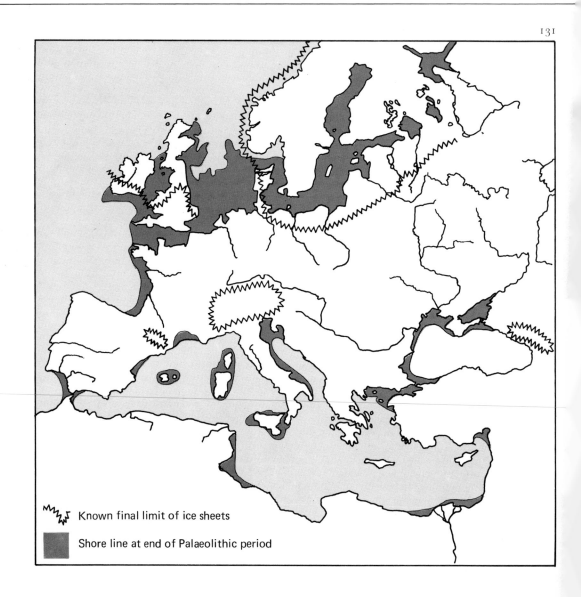

131

Known final limit of ice sheets

Shore line at end of Palaeolithic period

wards with the ice. Reindeer herds (page 48) roamed over France, and in central Europe the small stocky Przewalski's horse (133) was common. The birds, such as the ptarmigan, were also cold-loving, and arctic foxes once had their lairs in Surrey. One animal which became extinct during this period, probably because of over hunting by man, was the mammoth, an elephant adapted to cold conditions. Several remarkable finds have been made in Siberia, where whole bodies of mammoths (134) have been found buried in the permanently frozen bogs in which they drowned, their trunks subsequently gnawed by wolves. So perfect is the preservation that, in one case, journalists are reputed to have cut meat off the frozen carcasses and eaten it, claiming that at 20,000 years these were the oldest steaks in the world!

132 133
134

THE UPPER PALAEOLITHIC. Excavation methods have improved enormously since the early investigations at La Madeleine, the type site of the Magdalenian culture (135). Nowadays as at Combe Grenal (136) and Abri Pataud (137), stratigraphic units are carefully isolated and removed separately, and the implements and bones are measured as they are discovered. Such techniques have greatly increased our knowledge of the succession of Upper Palaeolithic cultures in Western Europe, though the broad outlines have been known since the end of the century (see Table III on p. 123). Upper Palaeolithic industries are characterized by the manufacture of long narrow blades, from which a variety of implements were made, for example end-scrapers (139) and chisel-like burins (140). A succession of phases have been defined and named after classic cave sites in France. The earliest major phase is the Aurignacian, which flourished in France from about 30,000 to

135

137

136

22,000 years ago. Solutrean industries about 20,000 to 18,000 years old contain beautiful bifacially worked spear points (141). During the latter part of the Ice Age, industries belonging to what is called the Gravettian phase, contained small pointed or rod-like blades with blunted backs, probably the armatures of projectiles or composite cutting tools (138). It was from the Gravettian phase that the famous Magdalenian culture began to emerge between 13,000 and 11,000 years ago,

with its finely worked bone and antler harpoon heads as those from Laugerie Basse (142). During this period, there was considerable regional diversity throughout Western Europe and Russia. It is still possible, though, to see some unity between all the various regional sequences, and the chronological and geographic diversity as the sway of fashion within a successful, artistic and inventive hunting civilization.

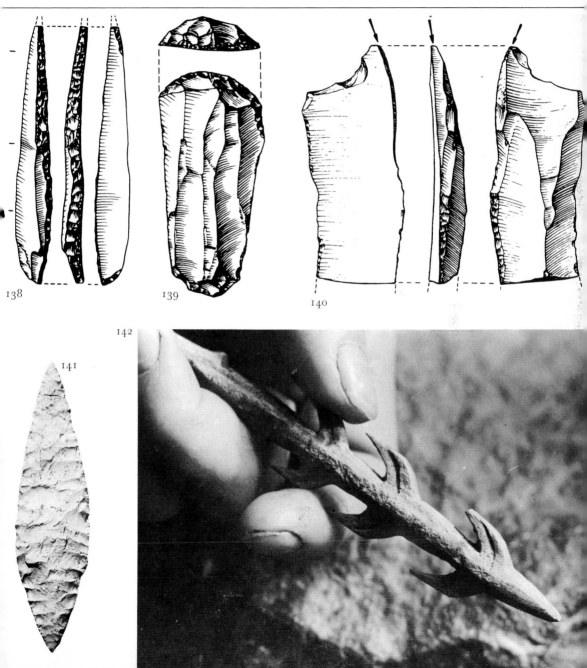

138

139

140

142

141

80 ECONOMIC LIFE. Inside a block of breccia from Christy's original 1864 excavations at Les Eyzies, in the Dordogne, France, there are flint blades, and the bones and teeth of animals which Upper Palaeolithic men had hunted and eaten (143). From an osteological study of such evidence, together with evidence from the art, we can reconstruct the diet of the men who lived in Europe during the last ice age, 30,000 to 10,000 years ago. They hunted mammoth (144), bison (145), horse (146) and reindeer, and followed the herds on their seasonal migrations rather like the modern Lapps do nowadays (page 48). They fished for salmon (147) in the rivers, and caught birds and other small game. There is little direct evidence regarding vegetable foods but, by analogy with modern hunters, this

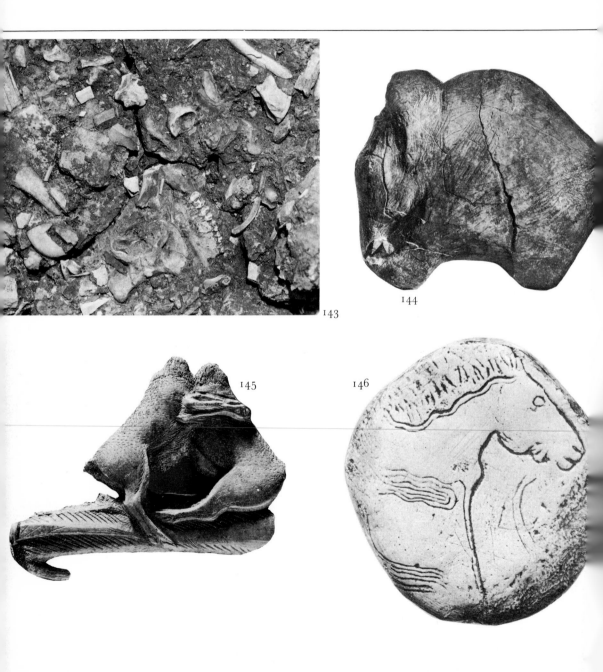

143

144

145

146

must have been a substantial part of their diet, and probably consisted of nuts and berries. Careful modern excavations have been carried out to expose whole living sites, such as the Magdalenian camp at Pincevant (148) near Paris. All stones, bones and evidence for structures such as hearths and post holes have been left *in situ*, and a detailed plan made of their positions. From such studies we can see the shape and construction of their houses, and even the plan of whole settlements. Their economy, group size, and possibly clothing was probably similar to that of modern Arctic hunters as this reconstruction by Maurice Wilson shows (149).

147

148

149

CLOTHES, DECORATION AND BURIAL IN THE UPPER PALAEOLITHIC. European Upper Palaeolithic people made bone needles, some of which are shown in (150), together with tools to manufacture them. A sliver of bone would be split and cut with flint saws, ground to a point with the stone rubber and the eye drilled with flint points. The needle would be given a final burnishing with the smooth stone and most probably used for sewing skin clothes against the cold tundra conditions, much as the modern Eskimo does. Shells and teeth had holes drilled through them (151) for use as necklaces. The foot prints in (152) are those of an Upper Palaeolithic man who walked on the soft clay floor of the Aldene cave in France 10,000 years ago, giving us an eerie link with those ancient hunters and artists of the last ice age. The dead were carefully buried. In (153) we see a skull being cleaned

150

152

151

in situ at Abri Pataud in France. In the Gravettian site of Dolní Věstonice, a skeleton was found lying in a crouched position (154). On top of it was the shoulder blade of a mammoth, carefully placed over the body after burial. One of the most spectacular Upper Palaeolithic burials was that discovered by E. Rivière in 1872, in one of the Grimaldi Caves near Monaco, south of France. At the Grotte de Cavillon, the skeleton of an Aurignacian man was discovered (155), dating back about 25,000 years. Around his head were two hundred sea shells, and twenty red deer teeth. There were more shells by his knees, and elsewhere in the burial were two flint blades and a bone tool. The bones of the skeleton were coloured with red ochre. This man was possibly buried fully clothed with a cap of shells, necklaces and other objects of value to him during his lifetime.

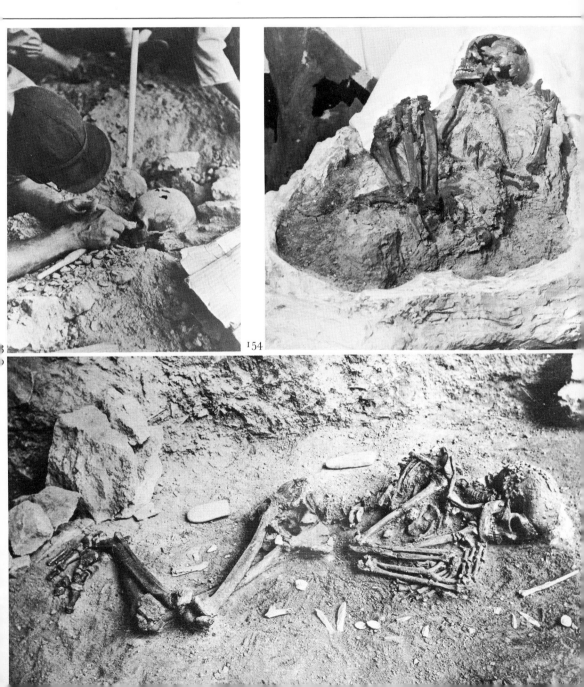

154

THE MAMMOTH HUNTERS. The clearest evidence we have for the way of life of Upper Palaeolithic communities comes from a group of Gravettian sites spreading east from central Europe to the southern Russian tundra. The layout of these camps is well illustrated by the results of excavations at Dolní Věstonice in Moravia. Here some 25,000 years ago a group of five living places was set up on the edge of a marsh (156), selected perhaps as a natural trap for the mammoth. Tens of thousands of mammoth bones together with those of reindeer and wild horse were found on the far side of the marsh (157) as well as around the living places themselves. One of these structures, discovered in 1951 (158), had a curved retaining wall of limestone blocks; a number of post-holes suggested a sloping roof (159). In the centre a well-constructed hearth was flanked by mammoth tusks. In and around

156

157 158

the hearth were more than 2,300 fragments of fired clay, the earliest "pottery" in the world. Many of these were in the form of the animals hunted, including the rhinoceros (160), bear (161 and 162) and lion. Several of these models, such as this bear's head (162), have stab marks impressed in them, as if their makers had intended them as some sort of Palaeolithic wax doll to stick pins into. A different kind of settlement can be found in southern Russia where long tent-like structures accommodating perhaps a whole hunting group were erected over shallow pits upwards of 40 feet long (163). These prehistoric versions of modern steppe nomads' skin tents were built over a frame-work of mammoth tusks and ribs, with the covering weighted down with skulls and flanked by shoulder blades.

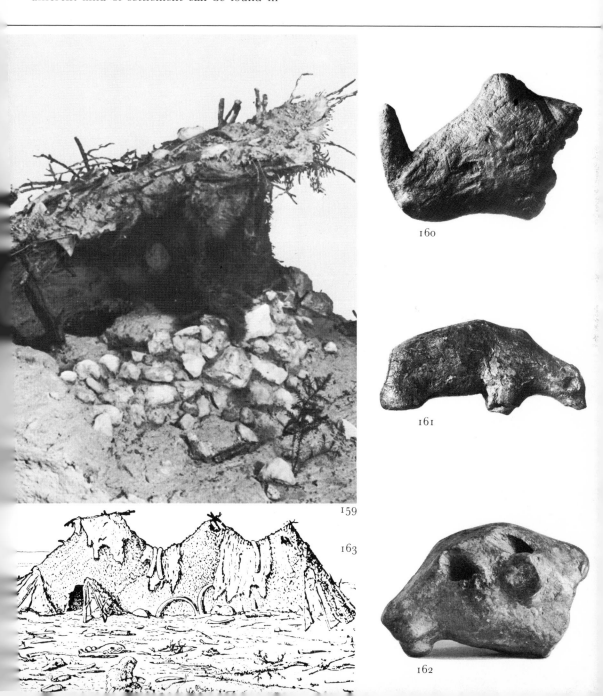

159

160

161

163

162

MAN DEPICTS HIMSELF. Although we have already seen that even chimps are capable of artistic expression, no art survives from before the Upper Palaeolithic era. Among the earliest and most remarkable art is the range of abstract female statuettes termed, with little regard to modern standards of beauty, "Venus figurines". These are associated with various local groups of the Gravettian culture stretching from France to Austria, Czechoslovakia and Russia. All stress sexual characteristics and some of them are pregnant. Facial features are reduced to a minimum. We may compare a figurine from Dolní Věstonice made from a fire-hardened mixture of powdered bone and clay (164), the rear view of a damaged mammoth ivory figurine from Lespugue, France, with long hair (165), a pregnant figure in steatite from the Grimaldi caves (166), and a figurine, not unlike the

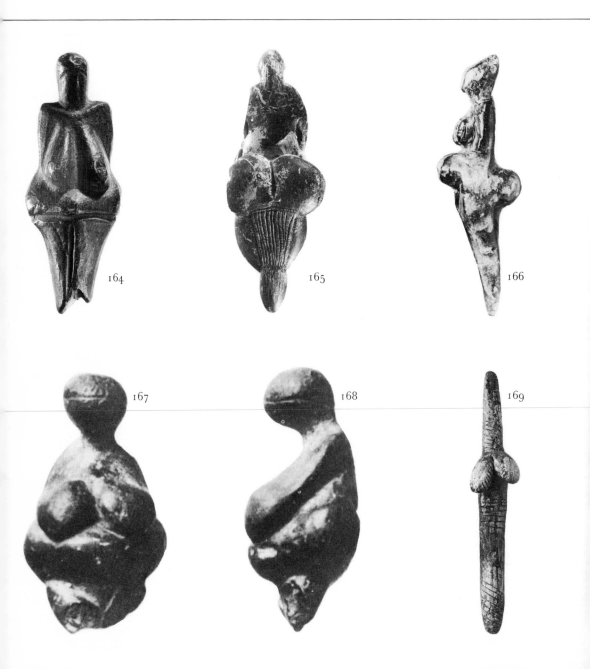

164

165

166

167

168

169

famous Venus of Willendorf in Austria from the Kostienki mammoth hunters' camp in south Russia, (167) and (168). Contrasting with these representations are some more heavily stylized examples from Mal'ta beside Lake Baikal in Siberia (169). The "Venuses" have been regarded as evidence of man's preoccupation with fertility and birth; they may equally be Palaeolithic pin-ups. There are occasional male representations, such as the unique jointed doll of mammoth ivory found with a man buried in Brno in central Czechoslovakia (170). Although there is no definite portraiture in Palaeolithic art, some pieces seem to come close to it as, for example in a tiny inch-and-a-half high ivory head from Brassempouy in the south west of France (171).

170   171

88 THE ART OF THE CAVES. The caves of Lascaux, discovered in 1940, demonstrate the variety of style and motif found in rock art, with complex polychrome "compositions", single outline figures and abstract symbols and schematized traps or dwellings (page 49). Recent studies of these compositions suggest that they reflect the artists' own understanding of the natural world, and that standard layouts were often followed. Occasional rough engravings on pebbles or slabs of stone such as one from Bruniquel in France (172) probably represent preparatory sketches. Low relief carving is also found (173). Although Upper Palaeolithic rock art is concentrated in southwestern France and Spain, recently, in the Kapovaya Cave in the Urals, archaeologists have discovered a whole range of animal drawings remarkably similar to those found in the west (page 50).

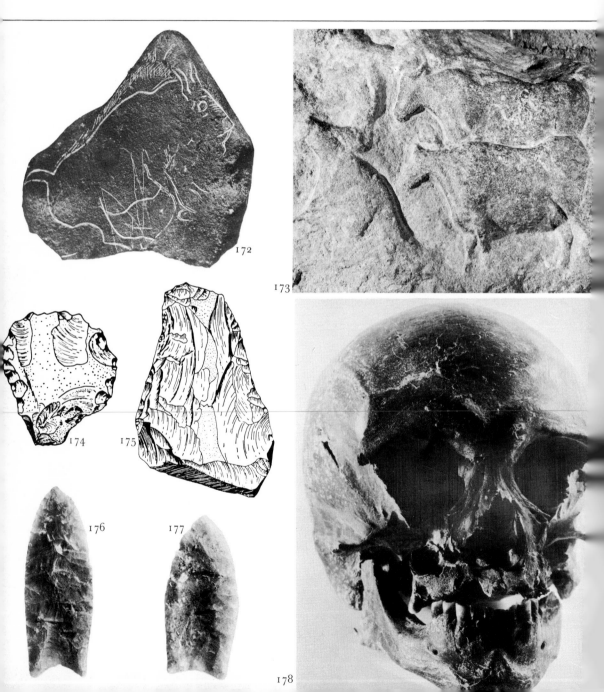

EARLY MAN IN AMERICA. There is considerable controversy over the problem of man's antiquity in America. Recent discoveries in the Peruvian Andes have shown that man lived there at least 20,000 years ago. The earliest South American industries consist of core tools and edge-retouched scrapers, (174) and (175). Some time about 14,000 to 12,000 years ago, a new stone tradition appeared, characterized by pressure flaked stone projectile points, such as fluted points from Arizona, (176) and (177). At Naco, also in Arizona, archaeologists are shown carefully excavating mammoth bones from a contemporary butchering site (179). The earliest known American skulls such as one from Tepexpan in Mexico (178) date from about 10,000 years ago, and are all *Homo sapiens*. The first American immigrants arrived, then, from Asia after the emergence of totally modern man.

EARLY MAN IN AUSTRALIA. Australia and Asia have been separated by stretches of water since the Tertiary period (after 60 million years ago). When and how man managed to cross the water and colonize the southern continent is still a question of active research. At Mungo, western New South Wales, between 25,000 and 30,000 years ago, there were people living on sand dunes by the shores of large lakes which have since dried up (page 47).

They hunted small marsupials, fished and collected emu eggs and shell fish. They made stone scrapers and cremated their dead. Even older evidence comes from river terraces at Keilor near Melbourne (180). On the east coast at Burrill Lake, a rock shelter (181) was occupied 22,000 years ago. The stone tools found in these and other early sites are characterized by heavy dome shaped "horse-hoof cores" (182) and steep edge scrapers. In some

180

182

181

sites in Arnhem Land, the world's oldest ground edge axes have been found (183) dating back about 22,000 years. During the last ice age both New Guinea and Tasmania were connected to the Australian mainland. In the New Guinea highlands, axes and other artefacts date back about 25,000 years (the occupation level is the dark layer in 184). The earliest men to arrive in Australia must have been contemporary with many giant mar-supials—such as the diprotodon, a creature the size of a rhinoceros, and kangaroos ten feet tall. These became extinct about 30,000 years ago, and it is believed that men hunting and burning the countryside added to their downfall. The cultural relationship of the earliest Australians to their presumed ancestors in South East Asia has not yet been worked out in detail.

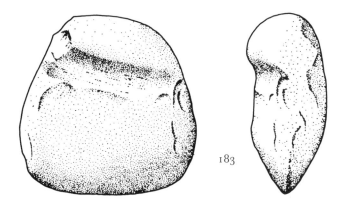

183

84

AUSTRALIANS BEFORE COOK. Modern Australian archaeology is gradually uncovering a sequence of technological developments, and a number of regional differences. About 5,000 years ago a range of finely worked flaked stone implements appear, presumably used to barb wooden spears (the bow is unknown in Australia). Some of the main forms of these implements may be illustrated from a collection made on excavations near Sydney (185).

With the exception of the leaf shaped Kimberley points found in the north and west (page 45), these types do not seem to have continued in used beyond some 500 years ago. Historical sources tell us much of the lives of the natives of the Sydney region, whose customs and artefacts were studied by the English explorers and settlers from the late eighteenth century onwards. A watercolour (186) shows a family fishing from bark canoes. The lines are tipped

185　186　187

with hooks made from the common turban shell as found on the shores of Botany Bay where Cook landed in April, 1770 (187). There is evidence of complex burial rites on a number of sites. A large cemetery of more than 100 graves at Broadbeach near Brisbane shows various different types of burials including "bundles" of bones (188). Although we do not usually think of Aborigines as constructing monuments, ceremonial stone alignments are found in a number of areas. In 1817, the explorer John Oxley discovered and excavated an earthen grave-mound near the Lachlan River in inland New South Wales (189). Beside the mound, which looks like a European Bronze Age round barrow, are two carved trees; another tree (190) clearly shows the use of a steel axe, indicating the rapid Europeanization of Aboriginal culture.

188   189   190

AUSTRALIAN ABORIGINAL ART. Modern research has shown that rock art in Australia is as old as that found in western Europe. In a large sink hole at Koonalda, several hundred feet down and in total darkness, large panels of parallel grooves cut into soft limestone walls were discovered (191). Charcoal from a hearth on the floor immediately in front of the markings was 20,000 years old, and this is believed to be the age of the art. Throughout the central and southern parts of the continent and in Tasmania there are several hundred rock engraving sites, with similar designs consisting of geometric symbols, and animal and bird tracks. Because of the extensive weathering of these, archaeologists think that they are many thousands of years old (page 54). At one site in the Cleland Hills in

191

192

central Australia, strange engravings of faces (192) have been discovered in heavily patinated rock, and these belong to the same ancient tradition. More recent, but probably still dating back several thousand years, are numerous cave paintings. The pigments are mostly red and yellow ochre, white clay and charcoal. Animals such as kangaroos, and hands and domestic implements were often depicted. Many galleries are dominated by strange human figures, often with elaborate head-dresses (page 50). Fortunately there are Aborigines who still carry on the artistic traditions of their forbears (193), and from them we learn that the paintings usually have deep religious significance, and that the cave sites themselves are the sacred dreaming places of their ancestors.

CHAPTER SIX

THE INVENTION OF AGRICULTURE

THE ORIGINS OF AGRICULTURE lie deep within the hunting way of life. Many primitive peoples who gather vegetable foods conserve and propagate the plants they collect. Some have taboos and other customs which prevent the over-exploitation of certain classes of game, and complex technologies have been developed for the preservation and storage of foods, such as fish, for later consumption during times of stress. Fire was used in early prehistoric times as it still is in places today, to clear the ground of shrubs and bracken, and to encourage the growth of fresh grass when the rains came. Other modern groups, such as the Lapps and the Caribou Indians, follow the deer herds on their annual migrations, culling their steady tribute, yet giving the deer some protection from other predators. Practically all hunting groups possess dogs, and the Tasmanian Aborigines of the nineteenth century A.D. are a striking example of a previously dogless hunting society adapting itself to take advantage of the new animal brought to the island by the Europeans. The American Indians both of the Prairies and of the Pampas found no difficulty in riding horses introduced by the Spaniards, and desert Australian Aborigines have been seen using smoke to tame camels to carry their baggage.

Nevertheless there can be little doubt that, about 10,000 years ago, fundamental changes occurred in the economic life of people in several parts of the world, and

that these played a decisive role in the subsequent history of man (see Table II on page 123).

In each case a series of cultural traits or practical inventions were developed which eventually transformed hunters into farmers. The most important factors seem to have included: control over the breeding of important food animals and the consequent selection of desirable traits; methods of herd management including conservation of the breeding stock, defence from predators, and extension of the natural habitat through land clearance, the setting up of watering points, and many other methods; the conservation, planting and eventually full cultivation of selected food plants, together with experiments in hybridization and selection of desirable strains; concentration of population into more sedentary settlements, leading to the foundation of villages; development of technologies for the harvesting and storage of food plants, for heavy duties such as digging and land clearance, and for the construction of buildings such as houses and stock pens. All these changes were associated with a dramatic increase in human population, which resulted in larger local groups, and led eventually to the formation of towns. There was a need for craft specialization. An economic surplus led to the development of trade, and to the support of non-productive administrative and elite social castes.

96

In the past, archaeologists have tended to concentrate their attention on the artefacts invented during these changes, such as edge-ground axes or adzes, pestles, grinding dishes, pottery and semi-permanent houses. The greatest exponent of this technological theory was the Australian, V. Gordon Childe, who, basing himself partly on the evolutionary sociological models of the American anthropologist Lewis Henry Morgan, coined the term "Neolithic Revolution" to describe these changes. More recent research has shown that none of the artefacts just listed are necessarily associated with this "revolution". For example, the earliest agricultural communities both in western Asia and in Middle America did not manufacture pottery; several old hunting societies such as the mammoth hunters of eastern Europe and the pre-historic Eskimos lived in substantial semi-permanent villages; and the oldest edge-ground or polished axes in the world now come from what are considered to be hunter-gatherer communities in Australia and New Guinea.

During the past two decades, archaeologists have begun to investigate the problem from an ecological viewpoint, seeing it as the gradual development of new relationships between man, and the plants and animals around him. American archaeologists in particular have applied the results of comparative analyses of different cultures to the development of agriculture in America and western Asia. They have proposed a sequence of related events beginning with what they call "incipient agriculture", practised initially to supplement the diet within the context of hunting and gathering economies. Agriculture slowly gained importance until the whole society re-orientated itself to practise the new economy, while hunting was maintained for a while as a supplement, or as a prestige or leisure activity.

Each local sequence has its own characteristics of course, but there is a general resemblance, both in the order and the timing of events from different regions. Many archaeologists have thought that the same cultural processes must have helped to bring about these transformations. Some have argued that the "Neolithic revolution" was only one step in an inexorable evolution of man's society. Others have thought that the changes in climate at the end of the last Glacial period meant that the most badly affected communities were forced to experiment with a new kind of economy. Others again see these major changes as having developed within the context of successful hunting and gathering societies, which had the means for experimentation and a high enough population pressure to take advantage of any improvements in food production. This is one of the most fascinating problems of modern archaeology.

WHAT IS AGRICULTURE? Man's gradual exploitation of plants and animals and especially his control over breeding processes were key factors in the "Neolithic revolution". About 11,000 years ago, in the Zagros Mountains of northern Iraq, a transitional stage can be seen in the organized herding of certain wild animals and a subsequent increase in guaranteed food supplies. The Lapps of northern Sweden and Finland with their economic dependence on the reindeer are a modern example of this stage (194). A long process of breeding was necessary before the sheep and goat—probably first kept as a stable source of meat—could be relied on, as in the Middle East today, to provide both milk and fleece (195). Although it was in south-western Asia that the first domesticated plants and animals developed, there were other independent "nuclear" areas for domestication—besides those of south east Asia and the Americas. By the fourth millennium B.C. the Mediterranean

194

195

climate of the then fertile Sahara was being exploited by pastoralists herding cattle, sheep and goats, as well as hunting animals such as the giraffe and elephant, as depicted in the rock-paintings of Tassili n'Ajjer (196). The Neolithic revolution depended not only on the skills of domestication but on technological aids to maintain control over nature. The development of the polished or edge-ground axe of stone or flint in Europe allowed the efficient clearance of land. This has been demonstrated by modern experiments using Neolithic axes (197). In *c.* 4000 B.C. the simple digging-stick illustrated in use in Highland New Guinea (198), evolved into a single-piece scratch plough or "ard" pulled by the now domesticated ox. Such ploughs, which are still extensively used in Asia and the Middle East (page 51), aided the more efficient tillage of light soils.

196   198

197

WANDERING HERDSMEN. We have just seen how the first stages of farming in the Old World developed among small groups of highland hunter-gatherers. The demands that certain domestic animals place upon their keepers are considerable; contrary to popular belief, a cow is by nature intractable, and considerable skill was needed before it could be fully exploited. Although there is no evidence of domestic cattle in Europe before 6000 B.C., the present-day process of Alpine "transhumance"—the stationing of cattle in hillside summer pastures and their subsequent wintering in the valleys (199)—probably continues the practice of Neolithic lakeside villages of the fifth and fourth millennium B.C. The possible independent development of nomadic herdsmen in north Africa has already been illustrated. Today, the Kirghiz of the broad highland valleys of Tien Shan in central

199

200

Asia or, further to the east, the Mongols of the dry steppe offer modern analogies for this way of life. Their portable skin tents, stretched over a light framework (200), are the descendants of the mammoth hunters' shelters of the Upper Palaeolithic. Complete mobility came only with the domestication of the horse. The hunting of the wild horse in North America led to its complete extinction. The bison hunt on foot depicted in Theodore de

Bry's engraving of 1595 (201) shows that the modern Redskin mounted band was in fact a product of white contact (page 51). Not until 2000 B.C. is there evidence of horse-riding in the Old World. The bodyguard of the Prince of Talat on the edge of the Ordos desert in Inner Mongolia (202) is the descendant of generations of mounted warriors whose movements west greatly influenced Europe's early history.

201

202

EARLY FARMERS OF THE OLD WORLD. Important evidence for the development of food-producing communities comes from the site of Jarmo in the Zagros Mountains. Here, around 6500 B.C., a group of some fifteen square huts were built of puddled mud on stone foundations (203). About the same time, close to a permanent spring, the first farmers at Jericho built round houses of sun-dried mud, defended by a stone wall with massive bastions and rock-cut ditch (204). Even more complex architecture and indications of religious ceremonies can be seen at Çatal Hüyük on the edge of the Konya plain in Central Turkey. The complex of houses dating from about 6000 B.C., each one built abutting on the next, are divided only by occasional courtyards. Shrines incorporating a whole series of bull's horns show the antiquity of bull symbolism in the Near East (205). "Tell" mounds produced by the superimposition of mud brick houses can be found in the Balkans as well as further

203

204

205

east. The first farming settlements in the Balkans, however, were simpler; about 6200 B.C. a village of pottery-making farmers was built at Nea Nikomedeia, in northern Greece (206). Several features of the pottery, clay figurines (207) and other artefacts point to the ultimately eastern origin of the community. In the Balkans, however, it was not only farmers who dwelt in well-constructed villages. On the shores of the Danube, at Lepenski Vir Jugoslav archaeologists have recently found a settlement of hunter-gatherers dating to about 5500 B.C. The houses each have a central hearth which is often surrounded by carved sandstone boulders with fish-like features (208). Once more in contrast, c. 4500 B.C. we see the rapid spread westwards along the fertile loess covered river valleys of the so-called "Danubian" Neolithic. At Bylany in eastern Bohemia, nearly a hundred long timber-framed houses covered an area of some 65,000 square yards (209).

206

207

209

208

LATER HUNTERS AND FISHERS OF WESTERN EUROPE. In the course of the tenth millennium B.C. the forest cover of Europe was increasing and extending northwards with the gradual warming of the climate. Rock-shelters once occupied by the Magdalenian hunters were now used by communities attempting to adapt to the new conditions. They still made harpoon heads but of staghorn like two from Yorkshire (210), rather than antler. These "Azilians" (so named after the cave of Mas d'Azil in the Ariège, France) painted pebbles with ochre (211). The post-Pleistocene, "Mesolithic", hunter-fisher groups settled near the rivers and lakes which covered the whole of northern Europe across what is now the Baltic and the North Sea. A typical settlement was excavated in a peat bog at Star Carr in eastern Yorkshire and dated to around 7500 B.C., the time of the first farming villages

210   212

211

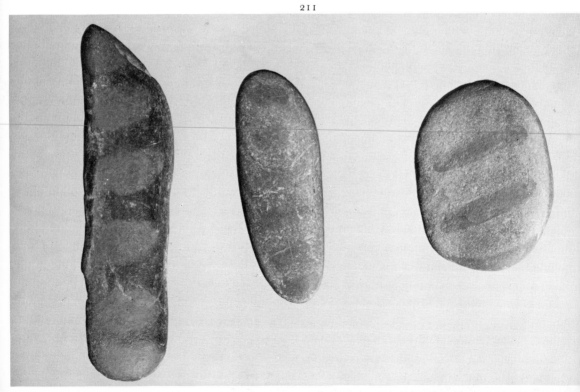

in the Near East. The peat bog had preserved a birch platform formed of logs cut with heavy stone axes (212), together with a whole range of fine harpoon heads cut from slivers of antler, flint implements and even the paddle for a dug-out canoe. Similar finds have been made in the peat bogs of Scandinavia, including wooden long-bows and arrow shafts with their stone barbs set in pitch (213). This "Maglemosean" ("big bog") culture also domesticated the dog, and produced minor but attractive carvings of animals and abstract forms from Baltic amber (page 52). From about 5000 B.C., coastal communities produced huge kitchen middens or shell heaps. These middens, such as that at Erteb∅lle in Denmark excavated between 1893–7 (214), contain pottery in their upper levels indicating the cultural influence of the first farmers to penetrate northern Europe (215).

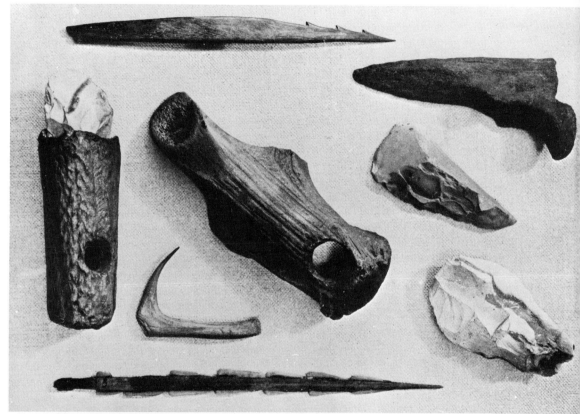

213

214

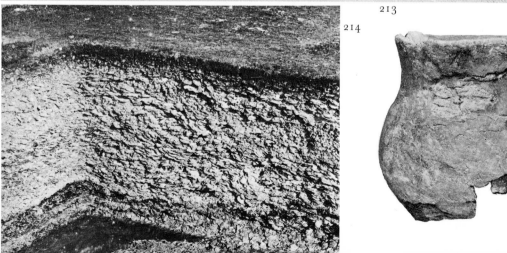

215

EARLY AMERICAN AGRICULTURE AND CIVILIZA-
TION. At the end of the Ice Age, groups of
American hunters and gatherers began to
cultivate a wide range of plants (see Table II
on page 123). The gradual development of
agriculture has been traced in excavations at
caves such as Coxcatlan in the Tehuancen
Valley, Mexico (216). About 7,000 years ago,
the cobs of wild maize were small, as on the
left of (217). By selection and hybridization,
the prehistoric Indians greatly improved the
size and quality of their cobs, and by 2,000
years ago modern maize had been developed,
as on the right of (217). Agriculture first
developed within mobile hunting and gathering societies. In the South West, ancillary skills
such as pottery making evolved. About 1000
A.D., Pueblo villages like Cliff Palace in
Colorado (218) were built, with its associated
black on white pottery (219). In Middle
America the domestication of plants led to
population increases and the foundations of

216

218

217

219

our high civilizations. In the Tehuacan Valley, Mexico, pottery was made into cooking and storage vessels, and also human figurines dating to about 1000 B.C. (220). Settlements clustered around ceremonial centres, the size of which can be judged from this temple platform at Cuicuilco, Mexico (221). The Mayan civilization was established in the jungles of Yucatan, South Mexico, about 300 A.D. Huge ceremonial complexes were built, and were the religious and adminis-trative centres for urban agglomerations. The government was headed by a caste of priests, as shown on a jade plaque (222). These cultures declined about 900 A.D., and were replaced by warrior communities, the Zapotecs (223) and Aztecs. In the northern Andes in South America, similar cultural developments occurred, including the construction of large ceremonial structures such as the Inca citadel at Macchu Picchu, Peru (page 53).

220

221

222

223

ASIAN HORTICULTURE. In tropical South East Asia, no great climatic changes were experienced at the end of the Pleistocene, and an essentially modern fauna and flora flourished there for about 40,000 years. The modern horticultural tradition is based on yams, and taro, a tropical plant with edible roots, cultivated in jungle gardens. This was supplemented by gathering wild vegetables and breeding pigs. The dominant late Pleistocene culture is called the "Hoabinhian", characterized by flaked and ground pebble tools; some are from North Vietnam, where the type sites are located (224). It is now believed that Hoabinhian people practised horticulture of some kind to supplement their diet and may also have begun to domesticate the pig. In Spirits Cave, Thailand (226), several plants including almonds, water chestnuts, betel nuts, peas and beans were intensively

224

225

gathered or even partially cultivated 12,000 years ago. Carefully worked quadrangular adzes (225) have also been found, and were probably used for wood working. In some Japanese shell middens, pottery has been discovered dating back 12,000 years. As research proceeds, it is becoming clear that in South East Asia and neighbouring regions, horticulture, pottery and the development of complex societies may be as old if not older than anywhere else in the world. These economies eventually spread throughout the islands of the Malay archipelago and into the Pacific. In New Guinea and on Timor, bones of dogs and pigs date back 5,000 years. In Kukuba Cave, Papua (227). a stone technology dating back 4,000 years was replaced by pottery around 2,000 years ago. Vast prehistoric agricultural drainage systems in the New Guinea highlands (228) are equally old.

228

CHAPTER SEVEN

MODERN HUNTERS

FOR ABOUT TWO MILLION YEARS, tool-making man earned his living entirely by hunting game and gathering wild vegetable foods. The invention of agriculture, and the demographic and cultural changes which it set in motion only took place during the past 10,000 years. About 15,000 years ago, the entire human population of the world consisted of probably no more than ten million people. Today there are three thousand million people. In spite of this three hundred fold increase since the introduction of agriculture, the period which preceded it was so vast that it has been calculated that ninety per cent of all men who have ever lived on this planet did so by hunting and gathering. The adaptive effects of this must be deeply embedded within our genetic history (see Table III on p. 123).

The last great expansion of agriculture took place during the past 500 years when European explorers and colonists forced their way into vast areas which previously had been the domain of the hunter. In North America, hunters were represented by the Indians of the western prairies and Canadian forests and lakes, and by the Eskimo of the far north. In South America, there were guanaco hunters on the Argentinian pampas, and fishermen and shell fish gatherers on the islands and fjords of southern Chile and Tierra del Fuego. In northern Asia, there were the bear and seal hunters of northern Siberia, and in tropical Asia, the vegetable gatherers of the jungles of the Philippines, Malaya, Southern India and Ceylon. In Africa today there are still such diverse hunting and gathering peoples as the pygmies of the Congo jungles and the Bushmen of the Kalahari desert. Prior to European settlement in south east Australia in A.D. 1788, the entire continent was occupied by Aborigines, some of whose descendants still practise their ancient craft in the western deserts and in Arnhem Land in the far north.

The life styles of these people are interesting to the archaeologist because they give tremendous insight into the life of all of our ancestors in the Stone Age. This is not to say that a direct analogy can be made between the Tasmanians of the nineteenth century and European Mousterians who lived 40,000 years ago. However, it would seem that all hunting and gathering societies are subject to the same ecological limits. A cross cultural analysis of modern hunting societies shows that, in spite of the diverse range of habitats and cultures involved, there is a basic core of similar behaviour which may have belonged to past hunting societies as well. This core which we could call "the hunting way of life" can be used as a model against which to test our archaeological evidence.

The hunting way of life can be reconstructed as follows: population density usually managed from about one person per two or three square miles in rich coastal and river districts, to as low as one person per 100 square miles in desert regions. Society was organized into bands, which were themselves loosely grouped to form tribes which shared most cultural traits including language. Bands consisted of several families and usually numbered between about twenty and sixty people. They were thus small enough to be mobile yet large enough to support children, old people and other vulnerable or non-productive members of society. These bands were the basic land owning and foraging groups, moving through the countryside in search of food. Movements were not haphazard, but were carefully organized so as to take advantage of seasonally abundant foods, and a series of base camps would be established from which to forage. There was a well marked division of labour. The men hunted, while the women gathered and also had a series of household chores such as collecting firewood, carrying water, making baskets and cloth, as well as looking after the babies and children!

The technologies to support these economies were usually simple, consisting of equipment for hunting, trapping, fishing and gathering, together with baskets and bowls for carrying and holding food, water and other personal possessions. Some societies had complex houses, watercraft and clothing. Others had the minimum of clothes and only simple lean-to huts. In general the equipment was limited by the need to carry it in the chase or when moving from camp to camp. However, at the base camps, semi-permanent settlements might be set up and possessions stored. Many societies used stone tools to cut flesh and to manufacture wooden implements. Although a study of the use of stone tools gives us insight into the uses of similar tools in antiquity, it also reminds us what a small aspect of the total technology they constituted. The wooden, bone, sinew and fibre artefacts, have usually decayed without trace in prehistoric sites.

In contrast to this simple technology, most hunting societies had complex social organizations and rules. Their art took the form of paintings on the walls of caves, on bark sheets and on their own bodies. They practised wood and stone carving, and had complex music, dancing and poetry. A detailed knowledge of the flora, fauna and other natural phenomena of their domains was essential for their survival. Myths and religions were created to explain the internal relationships of these phenomena.

The contrast between the simple technologies and sophisticated intellectual, artistic and religious lives of many hunting peoples serves as an apt reminder to Industrial Man that the "progress" of which he is so proud, can largely be measured in terms of accumulation of "objects". The "soul" of man has changed very little over tens of thousands of years.

Before Australia was colonized by Europeans, it was inhabited by Aborigines whose total population has been estimated at about 300,000 people, speaking some 500 different languages. One region where the original hunter-gatherer culture has survived is the Western Desert, a vast dry area of more than half a million square miles. The people are almost naked and live together in bands; the women look after the children and have digging sticks to obtain roots and other vegetable foods which they carry in wooden dishes (229). The men carry "woomeras" or spear-throwers, and boomerangs (230) with which to hunt kangaroos as well as a variety of smaller game. To manufacture their weapons and utensils, they use stone flakes (231) which are obtained from special quarries. The Tasmanian Aborigines differed in many ways from the Australians (232). This has led to speculation as to how they reached their

229

230

mountainous island, which is now separated from Australia by 200 miles of sea. Archaeologists believe that Tasmanian Aborigines have lived in caves such as those at Rocky Cape for 8,000 years; this undisturbed midden surface of 4500 B.C. shows that their diet included shell fish, seal, sea bird, and fish (233). It is most likely that the first Tasmanians walked across a land bridge from the mainland during Late Glacial times (20,000 years ago), and that the sea cut them off about 12,000 years ago. European explorers rediscovered the island during the seventeenth and eighteenth centuries and reported that the Tasmanians lived and foraged in small bands, building simple lean-to huts (234) in the dry eastern half of the island, and used catamaran-like rafts to cross the rivers. On the west coast, rocks such as at Mount Cameron West (page 54) were carved about 2,000 years ago and covered with drifting sand a thousand years later.

233

232

234

TIERRA DEL FUEGANS. The island at the tip of South America was named Tierra del Fuego by Magellan in 1520 because of the numerous fires which he saw there on the shore. To sailors rounding Cape Horn and battling against the fierce seas of that ice-bound region, it was a dreaded place and many mythical stories grew up about the human giants who were supposed to live there (235). Later scientific accounts by Cook and Darwin have given us fascinating descriptions of these hunters and fishermen. On the west of Tierra del Fuego, facing the notorious "Roaring Forties" gales lived the Yahgans. They built snug dome-shaped houses out of a framework of bent sticks covered with thatched grass (240). The *Nothofagus* or Southern Beech rain forests are dank and unproductive, so the Yahgans subsisted almost entirely on the sea, fishing and hunting seals from bark canoes (241). They

235

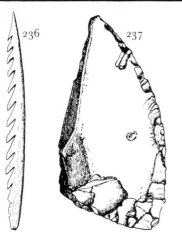

236   237

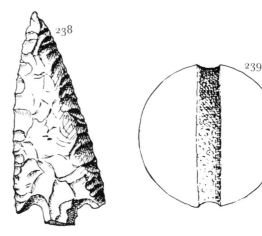

238

239

made bone harpoons (236) and used curved stone scraper-knives (237). The women dived for shell fish, and this resulted in the accumulation of huge middens. These maritime hunters had the distinction of being the most southerly native peoples of the world. On the east of the islands, there are open grassy plains, and on these the Ona Indians hunted the guanaco, a small animal related to the camel. Bows were used (242), with finely worked stone arrow heads (238). Guanaco fur was used for capes. On the Patagonian pampas, Indian tribes used horses introduced by the Spaniards to hunt the wild horse and guanaco in the open plains, as recorded by George Catlin in the 1850s (243). They caught them by throwing a piece of string tied to three round grooved stones called "bolas" (239), which entwined themselves in the legs of their prey.

2

3

TROPICAL PLANT GATHERERS AND HUNTERS. Although widely separated geographically and culturally, the tropical food gatherers and hunters of the world have very similar economies. These peoples live in the monsoonal tropical or equatorial jungles, and there are still small groups in the Malay archipelago, the Philippines, New Guinea, India, the Congo and the Amazon Basin, regions which are characterized by complex floral associations. The peoples' economies reflect this, and the bulk of their diet comes from gathering wild vegetable foods, supplemented by hunting forest birds and animals. To do this successfully, they have detailed botanical knowledge of the forests in which they lived. In the Amazon, small groups of gatherers live on the periphery of horticultural peoples (page 55), with whom they sometimes trade bush foods such as fish which they catch

244

245   246

with the aid of nets and poisons (244). A long blow pipe with a poisoned dart is used for killing small birds. In the mountains of Ceylon, the Veddas live in rock shelters (245), and hunt their game with bows and metal tipped arrows (246), though previously stone barbs were used. The people of the Oriomo Plateau in southern Papua practise a little horticulture, but spend most of their time hunting game such as wallabies and pigs, and gathering wild plants from the forests. Black palm or bamboo bows are used (247), with arrow heads made from beaten metal or sharpened bamboo. When foraging, they live in small groups. Their houses are made from a framework of forked poles, roofed with bark (page 56). They sleep on the floor or, in the wet season, on a platform under the roof.

ESKIMOS. The Eskimos are a group of hunters first described in the sixteenth century, who live in the polar region of Greenland, Northern Canada, Alaska and parts of northern Siberia. Their ancestors from northern Asia established themselves in this vast region over 4,000 years ago and developed a remarkable technology to fight against the harsh conditions. There are marked seasonal differences in the climate and hence in the food supply, and the technology is adapted to this. When the ice melts, they travel in light kayaks (248) to hunt seals and polar bears. In summer, tents are made from seal skins draped over a framework of wood or bone and pegged down with small stones (249). Large stone fish traps (250) are used to catch fish like the salmon, which migrate up the rivers to spawn. Some seasonal catches are enormous, and excess food is dried and stored for later consumption. In winter,

248

249

conditions are severe, and dome shaped igloos are built from blocks of ice and snow. In the most northerly regions, wood is scarce or absent, and animal products are used as substitutes. Sledges are made from frozen fish wrapped in seal skin for runners (251), and caribou antlers tied on with sealskin lines form cross pieces. Several layers of clothes are worn, with a heavy outer coat or parka, trousers, boots and muffs made from thick fur,

and undergarments of soft skin. One of the main domestic tasks performed by the women is to soften these skins by chewing them (252). They have well-developed visual arts including delicate sculptures in soft soap stone, and carvings in ivory and bone. (253) shows a bizarre wooden mask from the east Greenland coast.

250

251

252   253

THIS STORY has no end. Evolution is a continuing process as the giant reptiles of the Jurassic Period found out to their cost. Man is at a decisive point in his history. For the first time, he has the capacity to destroy himself totally (254). His population is increasing so fast that biologists have begun to talk of a "plague of men" (255). The surface of large parts of the earth has become a human artefact (256). His energy requirements are continually increasing and the pollutive side effects of his technology have even begun to threaten his health (257). While he stands for the first time on the Moon, glorifying in his genius, he is also reminded that spaceship Earth is circumscribed and finite (258). As archaeologists, we can look at man's present condition and place it within the context of his history over the past

254

255

256

two million years. For most of this time, his society was limited by a purely hunting and gathering technology. Man evolved physically and socially to adapt himself to these conditions. Then, over the comparatively short period of the past ten thousand years, as a result of his own inventive ability, many of these constraints have been lifted, and we have witnessed a dramatically accelerating rate of population increase and of technological and social change (see Table II on page 123). As we rush onwards, we might again contemplate the life of the savage not because of its supposed nobility, but because it represents man's most stable cultural adaptation. It remains to be seen whether or not it proves to be his most successful one.

257
258

TIME CHARTS

Table 1

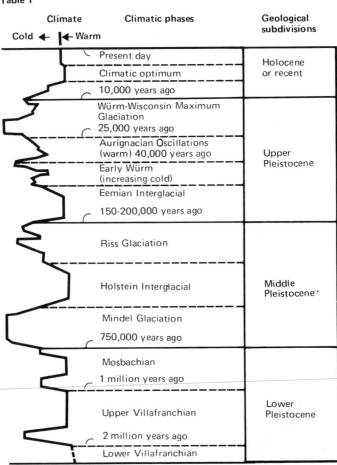

Climatic history and subdivisions of
the Pleistocene (after Chester S. Chard,
Man in Prehistory, McGraw - Hill Inc.,
New York, 1969)

Table 2

The dawn of man— from the first tool-makers to the establishment of civilization

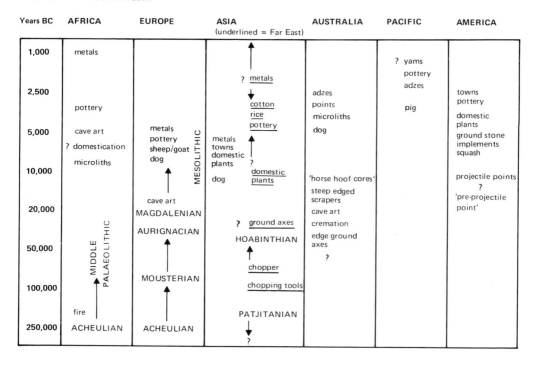

Years BC	AFRICA	EUROPE	ASIA (underlined = Far East)	AUSTRALIA	PACIFIC	AMERICA
1,000	metals				? yams pottery adzes	
2,500	pottery		? metals	adzes points microliths	pig	towns pottery domestic plants
5,000	cave art ? domestication microliths	metals pottery sheep/goat dog	cotton rice pottery metals towns domestic plants dog	dog		ground stone implements squash
10,000		MESOLITHIC	? domestic plants	'horse hoof cores' steep edged scrapers		projectile points ?
20,000		cave art MAGDALENIAN		cave art		'pre-projectile point'
50,000	MIDDLE PALAEOLITHIC	AURIGNACIAN	? ground axes HOABINTHIAN	cremation edge ground axes ?		
100,000		MOUSTERIAN	chopper chopping tools			
250,000	fire ACHEULIAN	ACHEULIAN	PATJITANIAN ?			

Table 3

The Main Palaeolithic Cultures

TIME (BC)	SITES		CULTURES (Europe/Africa)	FOSSIL MAN
10,000	Lascaux Laugerie Haute Parpallo Dolní Věstonice Kostienki Abri Petaud	Upper Palaeolithic — Magdalenian	Cave art bone harpoons and points antler	
25,000	La Ferrassie	Solutrean Gravettian Aurignacian	Specialized stone points and blade industries scrapers	Homo sapiens (sapiens)
	Le Moustier Mt Carmel Haua Fteah Shanidar	Middle Palaeolithic — Mousterian	prepared core implements scrapers, points burials	Homo sapiens (Neanderthal man)
50,000	Kalambo Falls			
100,000		Lower Palaeolithic — Hand-axe cultures — Acheulian	sophisticated hand-axes, some flake tools (viz., Clactonian)	Homo erectus (Pithecanthropus)
250,000	Swanscombe Hoxne Olorgesailie Terra Amata	Clactonian	? first surviving wood artefacts	
500,000	Somme gravels Chou-Kou-Tien	Abbevillian	early bifacially flaked axes	Paranthropus
2,000,000	Olduvai Gorge	Pebble tool Cultures	crude flaked stone (=oldest recognizable implements)	Australopithecus (Homo) habilis

FURTHER READING

THE LITERALLY UNIVERSAL NATURE of archaeology means that much of its published raw material is buried in learned monographs and journals in foreign languages. The following notes are intended as signposts to further sources and more detailed study.

A number of good general introductions to the aims and methods of archaeology are available, many in paperbound editions. Amongst the more recent are K. C. Chang, *Rethinking Archaeology* (Random House, 1967), Grahame Clark, *Aspects of Prehistory* (University of California Press, 1970), James Deetz, *Invitation to Archaeology* (Natural History Press, 1967) and Frank Hole and Robert F. Heizer, *An Introduction to Prehistoric Archeology* (Holt, Rinehart Winston, 2ed. 1969).

There is by now an extensive bibliography on the history of archaeology itself. Two "classics" are C. W. Ceram, *Picture History of Archaeology* (Thames and Hudson, 1957), and Glyn Daniel, *The Origins and Growth of Archaeology* (Penguin, 1967); a comprehensive two volume anthology with commentary is Jacquetta Hawkes (ed.), *The World of the Past* (Thames and Hudson, 1963). The recent advances in the uses of scientific methods are fully reviewed in Don Brothwell and Eric Higgs (ed.), *Science in Archaeology: a Survey of Progress and Research* (Thames and Hudson, 2ed. 1969).

Among older titles which lean particularly towards practical aspects of archaeology are Grahame Clark, *Archaeology and Society* (Methuen, 3ed. 1957), Stuart Piggott, *Approach to Archaeology* (Penguin, 1966), and Sir Mortimer Wheeler, *Archaeology from the Earth* (Penguin, 1956); Chester S. Chard, *Man in Prehistory* (McGraw Hill, 1969) also includes a brief survey of the development of ancient society on a world-wide basis more fully covered in Grahame Clark, *World Prehistory: a New Outline* (Cambridge University Press, 1969).

More selective world-wide surveys are offered in particularly well-illustrated form in Grahame Clark and Stuart Piggott, *Prehistoric Societies* (Penguin, 1970), Stuart Piggott (ed.), *Dawn of Civilization* (Thames and Hudson, 1961) and Derek Roe, *Prehistory: an Introduction* (Paladin, 1971). Two masterpieces of the study of the development of man in Europe, though mainly concerned with later periods than those covered here, are V. Gordon Childe, *Prehistory of European Society* (Penguin, 1958) and Stuart Piggott, *Ancient Europe: a Survey* (Edinburgh University Press, 1965).

For early America, there is Jesse D. Jennings, *Prehistory of North America* (McGraw-Hill, 1968) and Gordon R. Willey, *An Introduction to American Archaeology I–* (Prentice Hall, 1966––).

F. Clark Howell, *Early Man* (Time-Life, 1966) and David Pilbeam, *The Evolution of Man* (Thames and Hudson, 1970) study and lavishly illustrate the beginning of man as well as his culture; Sarel Eimerl and Irven De Vore, *The Primates* (Time-Life, 1966) is an excellent survey of our contemporary physical cousins. Useful illustrated books on the Stone Age are François Bordes, *The Old Stone Age* (Weidenfeld and Nicolson, 1968), J. M. Coles and Eric Higgs, *The Archaeology of Early Man* (Faber, 1969), and

André Leroi-Gourhan *et al.*, *La Préhistoire* (Presses Universitaires de France, 1968). Two books which also make use of studies of contemporary ethnographic communities are Bridget Allchin, *The Stone-Tipped Arrow* (Phoenix House, 1966) and Grahame Clark, *The Stone Age Hunters* (Thames and Hudson, 1967), while John E. Pfeiffer, *The Emergence of Man* (Nelson, 1970) brilliantly combines the evidence of primatology, anthropology, ethnography and Stone Age prehistory.

The series "Ancient Peoples and Places" published by Thames and Hudson, contains many important regional studies; to be mentioned here are Michael D. Coe, *Mexico* (n.d.), J. Desmond Clark, *The Prehistory of Africa* (1970) and D. J. Mulvaney, *The Prehistory of Australia* (1969). Special studies of particular relevance to various topics raised in the present book which illustrate the best use of modern archaeological methods are Grahame Clark, *Excavations at Star Carr: an Early Mesolithic Site* (Cambridge University Press, 1954), R. S. MacNeish, Douglas S. Byers *et al.*, *The Prehistory of the Tehuacan Valley I—* (University of Texas Press, 1967—), and D. J. Mulvaney and Jack Golson (ed.), *Aboriginal Man and Environment in Australia* (Australian University Press, 1971).

On Upper Palaeolithic art there is the beautifully produced study by André Leroi-Gourhan, *The Art of Prehistoric Man* (Thames and Hudson, 1967) and a cheaper though still well-illustrated volume, P. J. Ucko and Andrée Rosenfeld, *Palaeolithic Cave Art* (Weidenfeld and Nicolson, 1967), somewhat critical of Leroi-Gourhan's approach and covering a rather wider geographical area.

Finally, though of necessity there is never likely to be a perfect single reference book on archaeology, of use in different ways are Leonard Cottrell (ed.), *Concise Encyclopedia of Archaeology* (Hutchinson, 2ed. 1970) and Warwick Bray and David Trump, *A Dictionary of Archaeology* (Allan Lane, The Penguin Press, 1970). For those who want to keep abreast of some of the newest finds and ideas in archaeology are the journals *Antiquity*, *Current Archaeology*, *American Antiquity* and *World Archaeology*—published in England—*Mankind* and the American *Archaeology* together with those articles on archaeological subjects frequently published in *Science* and *The Scientific American*.

PICTURE CREDITS

INDEX